# THE SYMPHONIES FOR ORGAN

## Symphonie III

# RECENT RESEARCHES IN THE MUSIC OF THE NINETEENTH AND EARLY TWENTIETH CENTURIES

*Rufus Hallmark and D. Kern Holoman, general editors*

---

A-R Editions, Inc., publishes seven series of musicological editions that present music brought to light in the course of current research:

*Recent Researches in the Music of the Middle Ages and Early Renaissance*
Charles Atkinson, general editor

*Recent Researches in the Music of the Renaissance*
James Haar, general editor

*Recent Researches in the Music of the Baroque Era*
Christoph Wolff, general editor

*Recent Researches in the Music of the Classical Era*
Eugene K. Wolf, general editor

*Recent Researches in the Music of the Nineteenth and Early Twentieth Centuries*
Rufus Hallmark and D. Kern Holoman, general editors

*Recent Researches in American Music*
H. Wiley Hitchcock, general editor

*Recent Researches in the Oral Traditions of Music*
Philip V. Bohlman, general editor

Each *Recent Researches* edition is devoted to works
by a single composer or to a single genre of composition.
The contents are chosen for their potential interest to scholars
and performers, then prepared for publication according to the
standards that govern the making of all reliable historical editions.

Subscribers to any of these series, as well as patrons of subscribing institutions,
are invited to apply for information about the "Copyright-Sharing Policy"
of A-R Editions, Inc., under which policy any part of an edition
may be reproduced free of charge for study or performance.

For information contact

A-R EDITIONS, INC.
801 Deming Way
Madison, Wisconsin 53717

(608) 836-9000

RECENT RESEARCHES IN THE MUSIC OF THE NINETEENTH
AND EARLY TWENTIETH CENTURIES • VOLUME 13

Charles-Marie Widor

# THE SYMPHONIES FOR ORGAN

## Symphonie III

Edited by John R. Near

A-R Editions, Inc.
Madison

Charles-Marie Widor
THE SYMPHONIES FOR ORGAN

Edited by John R. Near

*Recent Researches in the Music*
*of the Nineteenth and Early Twentieth Centuries*

| Opus 13 | Symphonie I | in C Minor | Volume 11 |
| | Symphonie II | in D Major | Volume 12 |
| | Symphonie III | in E Minor | Volume 13 |
| | Symphonie IV | in F Minor | Volume 14 |
| Opus 42 | Symphonie V | in F Minor | Volume 15 |
| | Symphonie VI | in G Minor | Volume 16 |
| | Symphonie VII | in A Minor | Volume 17 |
| | Symphonie VIII | in B Major | Volume 18 |
| Opus 70 | *Symphonie gothique* | | Volume 19 |
| Opus 73 | *Symphonie romane* | | Volume 20 |

© 1992 by A-R Editions, Inc.
All rights reserved
Printed in the United States of America

*Library of Congress Cataloging-in-Publication Data*

Widor, Charles Marie, 1844–1937.
  [Symphonies, organ, no. 3, op. 13, no. 3, E minor]
  Symphonie III / Charles-Marie Widor ; edited by John R. Near.
  p. of music. — (The symphonies for organ / Charles-Marie Widor)
(Recent researches in the music of the nineteenth and early
twentieth centuries, ISSN 0193-5364 ; v. 13)
  ISBN 0-89579-270-2
  1. Symphonies (Organ)  I. Near, John Richard, 1947–.
II. Series.  III. Series: Widor, Charles Marie, 1844–1937.
Symphonies, organ (A-R Editions)
M2.R23834  vol. 13
[M8]                        91-759706
                                CIP
                                   M

# Contents

INTRODUCTION
   The Sources     vii
   Editorial Policies     viii
   Widor's Registrations     ix
   Critical Commentary     ix

WIDOR'S *AVANT-PROPOS*     xv

PLATE     xvii

SYMPHONIE III IN E MINOR
   [I] Prélude     3
   II. Minuetto     10
   III. Marcia     18
   IV. Adagio     26
   V. Final     29

APPENDIX 1
   [III] Marcia. Version *A/A'*     45

APPENDIX 2
   III. Marcia. Version *B/B'*, Mm. 45–114, 139–43     49

APPENDIX 3
   III. Marcia. Editions *C* and *C'*, Mm. 75–96     53

APPENDIX 4
   V. Fugue. Version *B/B'*     55

APPENDIX 5
   VI. Finale. Version *B/B'*     60

APPENDIX 6
   V. Final. Edition *C'*, Mm. 181–96     73

APPENDIX 7
   V. Final. Edition *D*, Mm. 181–95     74

Widor ca. 1887, the year edition *B* was published. The musical autograph shows measures 1–4 of Symphonie III: VI. Finale as they appear in edition *B* (see Appendix 5). Courtesy Music Division, The New York Public Library for the Performing Arts, Astor, Lenox and Tilden Foundations.

# Introduction

From the time of their first publication, the organ symphonies of Charles-Marie Widor (1844–1937) have been recognized as masterpieces. Their influence on subsequent organ literature was once immense. As new generations of organ music became popular, however, there inevitably came a time when Widor's symphonies were neglected, often being judged outmoded. Even the French Romantic organ, perfected by Cavaillé-Coll and adored by musicians, was abused by later generations. Sufficient time was required to pass before Widor's art and instrument could be considered from a fresh and independent musical perspective. That perspective has evidently been achieved, for in recent years increasing numbers of musicians have begun evaluating the symphonies on their own terms, with the result that the works have enjoyed a notable resurgence of popularity. At the same time, the French Romantic organ has regained its former status.

Widor was perhaps his own most demanding critic. Following the first publication of each organ symphony, a continual transformation was effected by the composer through several revisions. In certain cases nearly six decades intervened between first and last versions of a work. Even after the final published edition, Widor continued to scrutinize his organ works, applying finishing touches to the pieces that have constituted his most enduring legacy.

This comprehensive edition of Widor's ten organ symphonies is the first to incorporate the many final emendations made by the composer in his own copies. Here also are presented for the first time together substantially or completely different earlier versions of passages, sections, and complete movements as they were conceived by Widor in the course of his long career. Using information in the Critical Commentary and the music of the Appendixes, musicians can perform or study these several earlier versions of each work.

The Preface to this edition (vol. 11, Symphonie I) provides a full discussion of the symphonies' genesis and historical environment as well as an extended discussion of editorial policy, sources, and performance. In this Introduction are provided information on performance sufficient to give the reader a sense of Widor's own preferences in registration and expression (including a translation of his foreword, or *avant-propos*), a conspectus of the sources, a summary of editorial policy, and a Critical Commentary.

## The Sources

The original French editions and copies of these with corrections and emendations in Widor's hand form the basis for this critical edition. The locations of Widor's original holographs, if extant, are unknown. After extensively researching these works, the editor believes that all editions have surfaced, with one possible exception, noted in the Preface. These are listed here together with the identifying abbreviations used in the Critical Commentary and Appendixes. (More complete information on the sources appears in the Preface to the present edition.)

*A*      The first edition of opus 13, Symphonies I–IV, published in Paris in 1872 by the firm of J. Maho.

*A'*      A subsequent issue of *A* with minuscule alterations, published in 1879 by the firm of J. Hamelle together with the first editions of Symphonies V and VI.

*B*      The first complete issue of opus 42, comprising Symphonies V–VIII, together with the first major revision of opus 13, published in Paris in 1887 by Hamelle.

*B'*      A subsequent issue of *B* with small revisions to Symphonies I, VI, VII, and VIII, released between 1888 and 1892.

*C*      A new edition of opuses 13 and 42 (excepting Symphonie VI), published in 1901 and bearing the heading "New edition, revised, and entirely modified by the composer (1900–1901)."

*C'*      A subsequent issue of *C* that includes a new version of Symphonie VI and revisions to Symphonies I–V and VII–VIII, released by 1911.

*D*      A new edition of opuses 13 and 42, published in 1920, bearing the heading "New edition, revised, and entirely modified by the composer (1914–1918), (1920)."

*E*      The final published edition, again with revisions, issued 1928–29.

*Emend 1*      A copy of *B'* apparently used by Widor while preparing the revisions of edition *C* but also containing other emendations.

*Emend 2*      A bound and complete collection of single symphonies (representing variously the versions of editions *D* or *E*) with emendations made by Widor mostly after 1929, the year of edition *E*.

*Emend 3*      A copy of Symphonie V in the version of edition *D*, with numerous emendations by the composer, dated October 1927 in Widor's hand. This copy includes the revisions present in the 1929 edition, but it also contains further emendations, including some duplicated in *Emend* 2 and arguably entered after 1929.

*Schw*1–3 Gunsbach, France, Maison Schweitzer, MO 152, comprises a bound volume of Symphonies I–III in edition C owned by Albert Schweitzer, one of the students most esteemed by Widor and later his collaborator on the G. Schirmer edition of Bach's organ works.* On the first page of Symphonie I, Schweitzer has signed his name and written, "Les corrections à l'encre sont de la main de Widor" [The corrections in ink are in Widor's hand]. Since Schweitzer studied with Widor at different times over a long period, it is not possible to precisely date these corrections, but it is suggestive that almost all of them appear in print in edition C'.

Identical versions of movements in different editions are denoted in the Critical Commentary and the Appendixes by a slash between the identifying letters; for example, A/A'/B/B' means that a movement so identified remains the same through editions A, A', B, and B'.

## Editorial Policies

Edition E (or, what amounts to the same thing, a version remaining constant through edition E) is generally taken as the principal source for the main body of this edition. Sources for Appendix variants are identified individually in the Critical Commentary. All departures from the source either are distinguished typographically (when they are editorial and straightforward) or are identified in the Critical Commentary (when they derive from other sources or are not explained by policies described here). There are two exceptions to the policy of bracketing: editorial ties, slurs, hairpins, and directs are dashed; editorial cautionary accidentals appear in reduced size; all other editorial additions are enclosed in brackets.

The original French prints are themselves replete with cautionary accidentals, usually provided to cancel flats and sharps in previous measures. All except repetitious cautionary accidentals within a measure are preserved in this edition.

In the Critical Commentary the three staves of a system are indexed 1, 2, and 3, in order from top to bottom. Occasionally staff 1 in the source editions is congested, while an empty or nearly empty staff lies directly below. In such contexts this edition sometimes tacitly transfers left-hand voices to the open staff 2.

In the sources, indications of dynamics under staff 1 are sometimes duplicated under staves 2 or 3 or both in contexts where the Pédale and other manuals would have to share those dynamics in any event. The editor has suppressed most of these redundant dynamic indications. In addition, the old engravings frequently place dynamic indications over staff 1 because of space limitations on the page; conversely, they sometimes place tempo indications between staves 1 and 2 for the same reason. This edition tacitly regularizes the position of all such marks, putting dynamic indications within the system and tempo indications above it. There is an obvious exception to this rule: namely, when a dynamic is meant to apply to one staff alone, it appears closest to the affected voice(s)—therefore, sometimes above staff 1. Because Widor indicated registration and dynamics somewhat differently in editions A and A', the source placement of the relevant signs is preserved in appendix extracts from them.

Widor indicated staccato with the dot up to the late 1890s, but he favored the wedge thereafter. The two signs become mixed in passages partially revised by the composer after about 1900 (the period of edition C). Widor's pedagogical works on organ music reveal that both signs had the same significance for him. In the present edition all wedges are tacitly changed to dots in pieces conceived before Widor's change of orthography; wedges are retained in movements composed after the change.

Beaming in the original French editions is sometimes used to clarify phrasing. Beaming in the new edition follows that of the sources except when, under certain stringent conditions spelled out in detail in the Preface to this edition (see vol. 11, Symphonie I), it can be shown with great probability that inconsistencies arise through oversight or through adherence to an outmoded convention for beaming.

Characteristic of Widor's musical orthography is its attention to inner contrapuntal voices in every musical texture. At times this leads to a phalanx of stems all aiming for the same metrical position. Stemming in the new edition generally follows that of the sources, since the appearance of counterpoint, even in predominantly homophonic textures, conveys much of the "feel" and attitude proper to Widor's symphonies. Departures from the source are made only in clearly defined circumstances spelled out in detail in the Preface to this edition. In general, the number of voices in a measure is kept constant. In clearly homophonic contexts, where Widor himself is less strict, inconsistencies in the number of voices in a measure are usually allowed to stand. All editorial rests are bracketed. Stems added by analogy with parallel or closely similar passages are not bracketed, but the source reading is reported in a critical note. All other stems added to clarify inconsistent voicing are bracketed. Infrequently, superfluous rests or stems in the sources are tacitly removed to keep part writing consistent in a measure.

In conformity with accepted practice of that era, the original French editions of Widor's organ symphonies provide double barlines for all changes of key and for

---

*The pagination of this volume (3–6, 15–104) shows that it has been physically separated from a complete set of the symphonies. (Pages 7–14—all of movement II and the first page of III. Intermezzo from Symphonie I—are bound together with movement IV from Symphonie VI under accession number MO 162.)

some changes of meter. In this edition these are converted to single barlines unless there is also a new tempo, a new texture, or some other sign of a structural subdivision.

Reference to pitch in the Critical Commentary is made as follows: middle C = c'; C above middle C = c''; C below middle C = c; two octaves below middle C = C. Successive pitches are separated by commas, simultaneous pitches by virgules.

## Widor's Registrations

Widor generally indicated registrations by family of tone-color instead of exact stop nomenclature. In so doing he never intended to condone willful or indiscriminate interpretations of his registrational plans. He had a particular horror of kaleidoscopic stop changes and artlessly haphazard use of the Expression pedal. To those who indulged in a continual manipulation of the stops or Expression pedal, he habitually advised, "I beg you, no magic lantern effects." Barring the unfortunate necessity of making certain adaptations to varying organs, one should no more alter the "orchestration" of a Widor organ symphony than change or dress up the instrumentation of a Beethoven symphony. Clearly, the faithful realization of Widor's registrational plan is essential to the presentation of these works as the composer heard them. Beyond this, knowledge of the Cavaillé-Coll organ, the instrument preferred by Widor, will also prove useful to the performer intent on maximum fidelity to the composer's intention. A discussion of this organ and its constraints on performance can be found in the Preface to this edition (see vol. 11, Symphonie I).

To indicate the registration he wanted, Widor adopted a relatively simple shorthand system: **G** represents Grand-orgue (Great); **P** Positif (Positive); **R** Récit (Swell); **Péd.** Pédale (Pedal). Fonds are the foundation stops; Anches the chorus reed stops as well as all correlative stops included in the Jeux de combinaison. Pitch designations are self-evident.

When found above, within, or directly below the keyboard staves, a single letter instructs the organist to play on that particular uncoupled manual. When two or three letters are combined in these locations, the first designates the manual to play on, the second and subsequent letters what is to be coupled to it. For example, **GPR** instructs the organist to play on the Grand-orgue with the Positif and Récit coupled to it; **PR** tells one to play on the Positif with the Récit coupled to it; and so on.

When found under the lowest staff, one or more letters designate which manuals are to be coupled to the Pédale. When Widor employs only a dynamic marking in the course of the Pédale line, the performer should determine at his own discretion which Pédale coupler needs to be retired or reintroduced.

All crescendo and decrescendo indications, no matter how lengthy, are to be effected only by manipulation of the Expression pedal, unless the crescendo leads to a *fff*. In that case the Jeux de combinaison of each division are to be brought into play successively on strong beats: first those of the Récit (perhaps already on), then those of the Positif (sometimes indicated with a *ff*), and finally those of the Grand-orgue and Pédale on the *fff*. For the decrescendo they are to be retired in reverse order on weak beats.

## Critical Commentary

Depending on which of the six versions of Symphonie III (*A/A'*, *B/B'*, *C*, *C'*, *D*, or *E*) one examines, sometimes moderate, sometimes sharp contrasts are to be found. Movements 1 and 4 remained almost untouched through six decades; movement 2 twice received many small revisions; movement 3 grew from two pages to seven; the Fugue (formerly mvmt. 5) was removed; and an added Final continued to evolve through five editions.

Widor left only three fugues in his symphonies (those in Symphonies I, IV, and *gothique*). It is from Symphonie III that he discarded his only other organ fugue, preferring to end with the impassioned, rhapsodic Final, of Lisztian bravura. Widor seems to have swept aside old-fashioned polyphony in favor of his forward-looking symphonic style. In actuality, this symphony contains a wonderful blend of both styles.

### [I] Prélude

As a private student of Fétis, Widor wrote numerous fugues, canons, and other contrapuntal exercises. This movement is one of three in the symphony wherein Widor makes a happy marriage of "scholastic polyphony" and what he called the "new language" of the symphonic organ (see par. 6 of his *avant-propos*). The piece is written in four-part counterpoint, deftly colored for the modern organ. There are two similar versions: *A/A'* and *B/B'/C/C'/D/E*. Edition *E* is the principal source. All variants derive from *Emend* 2 except as noted.

CRITICAL NOTES

M. 25, staff 2, note 4 is c'-sharp tied to m. 26, note 1; staff 3, note 4 is E[-natural]. M. 35, staff 2, enigmatic 2 over note 1 in *C'* and *E* (faded from *D* pressing?). M. 43, staff 2, *pp* is above note 1—an error; it should have been placed to indicate the dynamic for staff 1 (the Récit) as in mm. 62 and 111. M. 45, staff 2, beat 1 has no f' quarter note—editorial addition of the note brings consistency to the contrapuntal voicing of the passage.

M. 52, staff 2, note 2 is d'-natural. M. 54, staff 1, lower voice, note 1 is c'[-flat] tied from previous measure. M. 56, staff 2, note 2 is c'-natural. M. 58, staff 1, the directive is **G** only—in this case **G** is being used as an abbreviation for **GPR,** which Widor states is his practice when it proves expedient (see Critical Commentary for VI. Finale of Symphonie II, found in vol. 12 of this series).

M. 64, staff 2, beat 1 has no e' quarter note (see report for m. 45). M. 66, staff 2, dotted half notes are stemmed together—edition follows stemming in parallel m. 47.   M. 98, staff 1, top voice, note 4 has sharp—an error resulting from an engraver's effort to improve the deteriorating plate; the faded natural was mistaken for a sharp.   M. 113, staff 2, beat 1 has no a' quarter note—see report for m. 45.

As stated in the Preface to this edition (see vol. 11, Symphonie I, "Performance Guidelines") Widor was less detailed in his use of dynamic markings in editions *A* and *A'*. This movement presents an excellent opportunity to study Widor's augmentation of these interpretive details, as well as his other small adjustments, since the only revision occurred between editions *A'* and *B*.

Version *A/A'* differs as follows. The registration is "Clavier 1: fonds de 16 et 8 accouplés aux anches du récit. Clav. 2: anches du récit. Clav. 3: Flûte de 8." The registration for the Pédale was evidently left out by mistake. "Cl. 1" is employed in lieu of **GPR** and its abbreviation **G**; "Cl. 2" in lieu of **R**; "Cl. 3" in lieu of **P**. Pédale couplers are not indicated. There is no metronome mark.   M. 5, staff 1, note 6 has no tie to m. 6, lower voice, note 1.   M. 12, staff 1, note 5 has no tie to m. 13, upper voice, note 1.   M. 43, staff 1, registration directive is "Oboe."   M. 45, staff 1 has no crescendo hairpin.   M. 46, staff 1 has no *p*.   M. 48 has no "anches" directive.   M. 62, staff 1, registration directive is "Oboe."   M. 64, staff 1 has no crescendo hairpin.   M. 65, staff 1 has no *p*.   M. 67 has no "anches" directive.   M. 71, staff 3, notes 1 and 2 have no tie.   M. 111, staff 1, registration directive is "Oboe."   M. 113 has no *rit.*; staff 1 has no crescendo hairpin.   M. 114, staff 1 has no *p*.   M. 115 has no "anches" directive or *a tempo*.

## II. Minuetto

To those who wanted Widor's organ works to assume a more religious character, this romantically tinged minuet, of an unabashed dance character, would have seemed the most secular movement in all of his organ symphonies. It exists in three similar versions: *A/A'*, *B/B'*, and *C/C'/D/E*. *A/A'* and *B/B'* are nearly identical; numerous small revisions produced *C/C'/D/E*.

More than half of Widor's revisions of the Minuetto for edition *B* continue the kinds of additions he had been making systematically to the symphonies: there are one altered and fourteen additional dynamic markings and four additional tempo indications. Besides these, Widor made seven changes of notation and seven changes of articulation (staccatos or slurs). By the time of edition *C* Widor had become dissatisfied, above all, with his original treatment of the Pédale: for that edition he made no fewer than forty notational revisions in staff 3, as compared to three in staff 1 and six in staff 2. At the same time he made five further changes of articulation (staccatos or slurs).* For the final version, edition *E* is the principal source.

The various pressings of this movement manifest a problem that plagues several movements in opus 13: small details like staccato dots, stems, and other fine lines tended to disappear from the printed page as plates aged and materials and conditions of printing varied. In the Minuetto it was staccato dots that were at greatest risk: in the final version of the movement (*C/C'/D/E*) they fade in and out of various prints in random fashion. In the present edition, staccato dots lacking in the principal source but present in other prints of the final version (as well as editorial staccato dots) appear in brackets without report.

In editions *A* and *A'* the return to the minuet after the trio is indicated by *da capo*. Beginning in edition *B* the *da capo* section is written out. The engravers apparently worked from the existing print, replicating it in every detail, except for the inadvertent omission of a few staccato dots (additionally, staccato dots missing from mm. 26 and 42 of the minuet—see critical reports—were supplied in parallel mm. 119 and 135 of the *da capo*).

This is one of the few movements where Widor uses a specific stop nomenclature in his registrational scheme that raises questions. Beginning with edition *B* he calls for "Diapason et Principal" in the Positif (*A/A'* has "Flûte"). Neither of the former stops are found in the Positif of the Saint-Sulpice organ, and few organs, if any, could offer such a selection. For the trio, where these stops accompany the Récit Trompette, Widor would have prepared the following (assuming that these stop names stemmed from his choice at Saint-Sulpice): Grand-orgue and Solo coupled to the Grand-choeur, with Solo Principal drawn. During the minuet he would have played the part marked **G** on a Flûte of the Grand-orgue; for the trio he would have retired the Flûte, drawn the Diapason (which is small scaled—almost a Salicional), and played the part marked **P** on the Grand-choeur (which, instead of the Positif, would be coupled to the Pédale); for the reprise of the minuet, he would have retired the Diapason, redrawn the Flûte, and returned to the Grand-orgue.†

### Critical Notes

M. 3, staff 1, lower voice, note 2, staccato added by analogy with m. 48—in this passage staccato is contextually appropriate, whereas legato is required for the lower voice in mm. 7–9 and 52–53; by extension, the note at the end of a slur in a concurrent Pédale part would likely be played staccato along with the right hand (e.g., note 2 of mm. 3, 7, 44, 48, and 52).   M. 7, staff 1, upper voice, note 5, staccato added by analogy with m. 52.   M. 18, staves 1 and 2, beat 2 has enigmatic *cresc.* directive in *B/B'* and *C/C'/D/E*—contrary to Widor's normal use of the directive, it might signify a preparation of the Swell box to make the four Récit notes of the next measures louder; this seems illogical, how-

---

*The tallies of revisions in editions *B* and *C* do not include reoccurrences in the minuet da capo.

†For a description of technical aspects of the Saint-Sulpice organ together with its specification, see Performance Guidelines in the Preface to this edition (vol. 11, Symphonie I, xxi).

ever, since a dynamic marking on the notes in question would be all that is needed. M. 21, staff 1, lower voice has dotted half note in all editions—to hold the note its full value, it is necessary to play it with the left hand sometime before the right hand transfers to the Récit, at which point staff 2 introduces a putative fourth voice (for Widor this is unusually awkward part writing) with a unison (enharmonically equivalent) b'-flat; by giving the a'[-sharp] a durational value that extends beyond the change of manual, Widor ensures that the note will be sustained rather than rearticulated when (for reasons of part writing) it is renotated as a b'-flat on staff 2; the present edition preserves a three-voice texture by subtracting the durational value of the staff 2 b'-flat from the value of the staff 1 a'[-sharp] and then editorially tying the two notes together.

M. 26, staff 2, upper voice, note 3 has no staccato in any edition—staccato added by analogy with parallel m. 119. M. 42, staff 1, upper voice, note 3 has no staccato in any edition—staccato added by analogy with parallel m. 135; lower voice, note 1, the accidental is indefinite in primary set 1 of edition *E* (see Published Editions in the Preface to this edition, vol. 11 in this series, Symphonie I, xiv–xv ["Edition *E*"]); in later pressings (those of the secondary sets) the accidental is a sharp— an error resulting from an engraver's effort to improve the deteriorating plate. M. 45, staff 3, note 1 is quarter note—an error; the half note became clogged in edition *D*; edition follows analogous m. 138 and editions *C* and *C'*.

M. 65, staff 3, upper voice, note 2 has enigmatic staccato in editions *C'* and *E* (but not *D*; faded from pressing?)—the staccato dot is in *A/A'*, where the note is not tied into the next measure; although deleted when the Pédale part was revised for *B*, the dot somehow reappeared in *C'* even after the Pédale part was revised a second time (to its present form) in *C*. M. 68, staff 3, upper voice, note 1 has staccato dot and note 3 has smudge over it in *E* but not in *C* or *D* (oddly, *C'* shows staccato dots clearly on notes 1 and 3)—when Widor revised the Pédale line of this trio for edition *C*, he removed the staccato dots and in many instances inserted rests between intervals requiring a leap for the right foot; even where he did not specify rests between leaps, detached pedaling is mandatory and obviates the need for staccato dots; it is the editor's belief that the few staccatos remaining in these measures in one edition or another are the result of faulty plates. M. 75, staff 1, upper voice, note has no dot in *B/B'* and *C/C'/D/E*—an error. M. 79, staff 2, beat 2 has eighth rest.

M. 96, staff 1, lower voice, note 2, staccato added by analogy with m. 48—see report for parallel m. 3. M. 100, staff 1, upper voice, note 5, staccato added (as in parallel m. 7) by analogy with m. 52. M. 110, staff 3, note 2 is quarter note in *E*—an error; edition follows editions *B* through *D*. M. 111, staves 1 and 2, beat 2 has enigmatic *cresc.* directive in *B/B'* and *C/C'/D/E*—see report for parallel m. 18. M. 114, staff 1, lower voice has dotted half note in all editions—see report for parallel m. 21; staff 2, note 5, staccato added by analogy with parallel m. 21.

M. 122, staff 2, upper voice, staccatos added by analogy with parallel m. 29. M. 157, staff 1, beat 1, grace notes are engraved before the barline in *B/B'* and *C/C'/D/E*—edition follows Widor's usual practice.

## III. Marcia

Widor had numerous opportunities during the church year, especially on high feast days, to accompany great processions at Saint-Sulpice. Like the Marche pontificale (Symphonie I), the Marcia clearly evokes the majestic aura of one of those occasions. The former march is set in the strong organ key of C major; here the music is lifted to the brilliant and relatively exotic organ key of F-sharp major. There are five versions of this movement: *A/A'*, *B/B'*, *C*, *C'*, and *D/E*. Version *A/A'*, one hundred measures in length, was expanded in edition *B* to 143 measures; the new material seems more improvised than composed. Widor must have sensed this himself as edition *C* contains a complete revision of the new material, expanding the movement to 163 measures. Even though Widor seems to have repudiated the *B/B'* version by revising it so thoroughly, it is this version that J. Hamelle republished unaltered in 1934 under the title "Marcia (extraite de la 3$^{me}$ Symphonie)" (plate no. J.7693.H).

Edition *C'* differs from *C* in minor ways in measures 76–95. Widor sometimes became fixated on certain passages where he seemed unable to make up his mind; he would return to the same measures time and time again. Version *D/E* is similar to edition *C'*, though again with further adjustments in measures 76–95. Version *A/A'* can be found in Appendix 1, the unique passages of version *B/B'* in Appendix 2, and an excerpt from editions *C* and *C'* in Appendix 3. For the final version, edition *E* is the principal source.

In this movement the music moves rather freely between homophonic and contrapuntal textures, making it interesting to study in terms of Widor's treatment of part writing. In contrapuntal textures several editorial rests and stems have been added to keep stable the number of voices in a given measure. In the homophonic passages Widor's stemming practice, which is sometimes curious there, has been allowed to stand. For a full explanation of the editorial policies regarding this matter, see "Contrapuntal Voicing" in the Preface to this edition (vol. 11, Symphonie I, xix).

### Critical Notes

M. 1, a repeat bar appears before the first full measure in all editions—it should have been deleted after *A/A'*, which has *da capo* and a complementary repeat bar at the end. M. 12, staff 1, beat 4, editorial slur added by analogy with m. 138. Mm. 22 and 23, *sf* marks follow analogous mm. 148 and 149. M. 29, staff 3, beat 4, the directive to change the registration (placed under m. 31, beat 2 in the source) reads "**GPR Péd.** Fonds" in *C*, *C'*, and *D/E*—the inclusion of **R** in the directive seems to be an error: if the Récit Anches are to be retired, this should occur at the double bar in m. 29, not in the middle of the passage being played on the Récit (*A/A'* has no registration change; *B/B'* calls only for "**Péd.** Fonds"); the editor has deleted **R** from the directive and moved the latter to a position more convenient for making a change of registration.

M. 31, staff 1, lower voice, beat 1, *A/A'* has quarter rest (as bracketed)—it was no doubt inadvertently omitted when the movement was reengraved for edition *B*. M. 32, staff 2, upper voice, notes are staccato in *A/A'* (but not in parallel m. 40). M. 44, staff 1, note 2 (unison f'[-sharp]) has no lower stem—stem added by analogy with m. 36. M. 45, staff 3, note 3, editorial natural follows *A/A'*.

Mm. 84–95, beat 3, staff 2 uses alto clef in *C*, *C'*, and *D/E*. M. 92, staff 2, lower voice, note has enigmatic slur or tie from m. 91, located on the previous page, where there is, however, no beginning for such an indication. M. 115, staff 2, beat 4, middle voice is stemmed with upper voice; separate stemming conforms to the majority voicing in the passage.

M. 155, staff 1, beat 1, the two notes are stemmed together—this is inconsistent with the separate stemming of the staff 2 notes; edition follows analogous m. 29.

## IV. Adagio

A linearly conceived movement, the Adagio is written almost entirely in four parts with the soprano and tenor in canon at the octave, separated by the interval of one measure. The movement exists in two nearly identical versions: *A/A'* and *B/B'/C/C'/D/E*. The movement is titled "Andantino" in *A/A'* (without metronome mark). The registration in *A/A'* is "Clavier 1: flûte 8 accouplée au Clav. 2. Clav. 2: gambes et bourdons de 8. Pédale: basse de 16 et 8" (no Pédale couplers are indicated). Small notational differences occur in parallel measures 12 and 48, where staff 1, lower voice, beat 2 has tied b quarter note, a eighth note; and in measures 66–75, where the slightly different staff-2 melody is an octave lower and still played on Clavier 1 coupled with Clavier 2 and where staff 1 is different in measures 69 and 70. For the final version, edition *E* is the principal source.

### Critical Notes

M. 48, beat 2, *pp* is at m. 49, beat 1—edition follows analogous m. 12. M. 51, beat 1 has compact "*cresc.*" only—expansion of directive through m. 53 follows layout in analogous mm. 15–17. M. 53, beat 2, *f* is at m. 54, beat 1—edition follows analogous m. 17.

## V. Final

Symphonie III has five movements in editions *A* and *A'*, the last movement being a Fugue (described below under Appendix 4). The present Final first appeared in edition *B* as the sixth movement, the Fugue being retained as the fifth movement. With edition *C*, however, the Fugue was deleted, and the Final became the fifth movement. It exists in five versions: *B/B'*, *C*, *C'*, *D*, and *E*. While the themes and general character of the movement are clearly established in edition *B*, it can only be viewed as a preliminary draft when compared with the version of edition *C*, which was extensively revised from beginning to end. This version is contemporary with Widor's last two organ symphonies (the *gothique* and *romane*), and it is in every way on an equal level of inspiration. Further refinements were effected in edition *C'*, which is identical (with the exception of one detail) to *D* and *E* until the concluding Moderato section, where all three editions differ. Widor had some trouble molding this last half page to his satisfaction. The "preliminary draft" version, *B/B'*, is given as Appendix 5. The slightly extended concluding Moderato sections of editions *C'* and *D* are given as Appendixes 6 and 7. For the final version, edition *E* is the principal source.

Editions *C* through *E* carry no metronome mark; the tempo mark of version *B/B'* is Allegro molto quasi presto, half note equals 96.

### Critical Notes

M. 3, staff 1, beat 2, tied a' has no dot in any edition—an error; staff 2, note 1 has no upstem—stem added by analogy with m. 7. M. 4, staff 1, lower voice, note 2 has no upstem—stem added by analogy with m. 3; beat 4, note has no upstem—stem added by analogy with m. 3; staff 2, note 1 has no upstem—stem added by analogy with m. 8. M. 28, staff 2, Widor writes "Cresc" over note 2 in *Schw*1–3 (see plate 1)—this placement aligns with the phrase repetition more accurately than does the hairpin in the source. M. 30, staff 3, note 2 is dotted in editions *C'* through *E*—an error; the dot was not deleted after the note was revised from dotted half note of edition *C*.

M. 31, the emendation in *Schw*1–3 (see plate 1) approaches the reading found in editions *D* and *E* but differs from it in an interesting way. In the final reading an e" eighth note and g"-natural dotted quarter note in staff 2 show the performer that the left hand takes the right-hand part at the moment the right hand moves from **R** to **GPR.** The resulting redundancy between the g"-naturals on staves 1 and 2, beat 3 (both being played on **GPR**), is a rarity in Widor's writing, and, as plate 1 shows, was not how the composer first considered notating the measure. Widor evidently abandoned the simpler notation seen there because he felt it preferable to show how the passage could be played.

M. 54, staff 3, beat 3, rest has no dot—an error. M. 64, staff 1, upper voice, beat 1, note has no dot in any edition—an error. M. 65, staff 1, upper voice, beat 4, notes 1–4 are beamed as sixteenth notes; the ratio sign 4 over the beam has faded from the source plate—edition follows editions *C* through *D* and analogous m. 71. M. 71, staff 1, upper voice, beat 2, notes 1–4 are beamed as sixteenth notes. M. 81, staff 1, upper voice, note 2 has no downstem—stem added by analogy with m. 78. M. 85, staff 2, beat 3, note is not in any edition.

M. 92, staff 2, note 1 has no downstem—stem added by analogy with m. 88.

M. 119, staff 2, note 1 has no downstem—stem added by analogy with m. 123. M. 120, staff 2, note 1 has no downstem—stem added by analogy with m. 124. M. 122, staff 1, upper voice, note 1 is dotted in all editions—an error; beat 4, e″-sharp is stemmed both up and down in all editions—an error. M. 125, staff 1, beat 2, tied d″[-sharp] has no dot in any edition—an error. M. 137, beat 1, Widor writes "Crescendo" in *Schw*1–3. M. 146, beat 1, Widor writes "Diminuendo" (extending through m. 147, beat 1) in *Schw*1–3; staff 1, upper voice, beat 3, note has no dot in any edition—an error.

M. 150, staff 1, upper voice, beat 3, note has no dot in any edition—an error. M. 152, beat 1, Widor writes "meno vivo" in lieu of *poco riten.* in *Schw*1–3. M. 154, *p* is between staves 2 and 3 at beat 2 but seems mislocated—edition follows Widor's placement of the dynamic in *Schw*1–3; staff 1, beat 3, lower note of dyad has no dot—this is due to a faulty pressing or to plate deterioration. Mm. 164–65, Widor inserts a crescendo hairpin extending from the anacrusis to m. 164, beat 3, to the end of m. 165 in *Schw*1–3. M. 166, beat 3, Widor writes "Boîte fermée" above staff 1 in *Schw*1–3. M. 173, staff 3, beat 3, rest has no dot—an error. M. 175, staff 1, lower voice, note 1 has no eighth flag—an error; staff 3, beat 1, rest has no dot—an error. M. 177, staff 2, beat 2, e eighth note is not tied to e dotted half note—edition follows editions C through D. M. 185, staff 3, note 1 has no dot—an error. Mm. 186–76 have (♪ = ♩) as the metrical equation.

*Appendix 1*

[III] *Marcia. Version A/A'*. Edition *A'* is the principal source.

M. 40, staff 2, upper voice, notes 1–2, staccato added by analogy with m. 32. M. 44, staff 1, note 2 (unison f′[-sharp]) has no lower stem—stem added by analogy with m. 36. M. 45, staff 1, beat 4, note has no downstem—added by analogy with m. 49. M. 47, staff 2, upper voice, rest 1 is quarter rest on beat 2. M. 51, staff 2, upper voice, rest 1 is quarter rest on beat 2. M. 56, staff 3, beat 3, note has natural—an error.

*Appendix 2*

*III. Marcia. Version B/B'*, mm. 45–114, 139–43. To perform this version complete, play mm. 1–44 of version D/E, noting the variants reported below; then mm. 45–114 of this Appendix; then mm. 135–58 of version D/E; and finally mm. 139–43 of this Appendix. Edition *B'* is the principal source.

M. 47, staff 2, upper voice, rest 1 is quarter rest on beat 2. M. 49, staves 1 and 2, crescendo hairpin begins on beat 2—edition follows analogous m. 53. M. 51, staff 2, upper voice, rest 1 is quarter rest on beat 2. M. 81, staff 3, note 1 has no dot—an error. M. 110, staff 3, note 1 has no dot—an error.

Measures 1–44 in *B/B'* differ from *D/E* as follows. M. 16, staff 1, beat 4 has lower octave notes only, without staccato. M. 17, staff 1, beat 1, dyad is c″[-sharp]/f″[-sharp]. M. 18, staff 1, beat 4 has lower octave notes only (staccato). M. 19, staff 1, beat 1 has lower octave note only (staccato). M. 29, beat 4, directive reads "**Péd.** Fonds" and is placed under m. 31, beat 3.

Measures 115–38 in *B/B'* differ from version *D/E* as follows (measure numbers are those of *B/B'*; to obtain measure numbers for *D/E*, add 20 to the *B/B'* measure numbers). M. 122, staff 1, beat 4 has lower octave notes only, without staccato. M. 123, staff 1, beat 1, dyad is c″[-sharp]/f″[-sharp]. M. 124, staff 1, beat 4 has lower octave notes only (staccato). M. 125, staff 1, beat 1 has lower octave note only (staccato). Mm. 128 and 129, beat 1 has no *sf* directives. Mm. 135–36, beat 3, directive reads "*poco meno vivo*" only. M. 136, beat 4 through m. 138, staff 3, all notes are doubled an octave higher.

*Appendix 3*

*III. Marcia.* Editions C and C', mm. 75–96. Edition C' variants appear as *ossia*s.

To perform edition C or C' complete, play measures 1–74 of version *D/E*, then this Appendix, then measures 97–163 of version *D/E*.

Mm. 84–95, beat 3, staff 2 uses alto clef in both editions.

*Appendix 4*

*V. Fugue. Version B/B'*. The Fugue survived in Symphonie III through two similar versions: *A/A'* and *B/B'*. While its subject is rhythmically alluring, especially in the first full measure, the working-out of the material seems to the editor a bit pedestrian. Widor undoubtedly realized that the piece did not bring the symphony to a successful conclusion, for he composed a vigorous and novel Finale for edition B. In juxtaposition to the new movement, the Fugue must have seemed anachronistic; it was deleted from the symphony in edition C. Nonetheless, Widor evidently thought enough of this Fugue to have it and the deleted Scherzo from Symphonie II printed together as *Deux pièces pour grand orgue*—published about 1910 by J. Hamelle, Paris (plate nos. J.5899–5900.H). (See commentary to V. Final for more on the history of the Fugue in Symphonie III.) Edition *B'* is the principal source.

An archaic and nowadays uncommon notational device is found in the original editions of this piece. In the second full measure of the subject (and wherever it appears in the course of the Fugue), the half note, rather than being tied to the first note of the eighth-note ligature, appears untied, and instead a dot is physically located in the position of the tied eighth note. When the Fugue was republished in *Deux pièces*, the publisher changed—but only in measure 2—to the modern convention found throughout the present edition.

There are no manual changes in *A/A'*. The present edition uses **GPR** in lieu of the **G** directive in *B/B'*, as-

xiii

suming terraced dynamics to be in effect and recalling Widor's practice of abbreviating the longer directive in certain contexts. The use of Pédale couplers is at the organist's discretion.

M. 11, staff 1, lower voice, note 2 is half note—an error.

## Appendix 5

*VI. Finale. Version B/B'.* This movement employs a notational convention frequently encountered in prints from the first half of the nineteenth century (not to mention the eighteenth) but fairly uncommon in music published as late as 1887. In common time, beat 4 of measure 2 looks like an ordinary binary division of the beat: eighth rest followed by eighth note. But according to the convention just mentioned, note values can be other than they appear: in the present example the actual rhythm of the binary division is determined not only by its literal notation but also by the prevailing ternary subdivision of the beat, established here—as often elsewhere—by an etudelike figuration or accompanimental pattern (for another example, see Appendix 2, m. 57, staff 1).

Evidence of this convention can be found in measures 3–13, which leave no doubt that, despite the meter signature 𝄴, 𝄾♪ can only be played 𝄾𝄾♪. Similarly, ♩.♪ can only be played ♩.♪♪. In these measures, then, the binary notation has already been adapted to the prevalent motion in sextuplets.

This reading of the binary meter should clearly be maintained in measures 14–29. There the characteristic anacrusis-and-strong-beat motive moves to the staff below the sextuplet figuration, where it can be more easily mistaken for a notation signifying two-against-three.

The convention ends with the arrival of the tonic pedal and a new theme beginning at measure 30. Whereas the opening theme grows out of the figuration, the second theme contrasts with that figuration. For the contrast to be effective here (mm. 31 and 33 as well as all derivative later passages), the binary division of beat 4 into two eighth notes must be taken literally; in this case, two-against-three is correct.

All this is confirmed by edition *C*, where Widor changed the meter to $\frac{12}{8}$ and adopted a precise notation that rules out a two-against-three interpretation for eighth notes in version *B/B'*—except for those in the second theme, first heard at measure 30. Edition *B'* is the principal source.

M. 34, staff 1, note 1 is stemmed up and down—this is inconsistent with the part writing elsewhere in this passage. M. 53, staff 2, slur ends on note 8. M. 128, staff 2, beat 1 has quarter rest—this is inconsistent with Widor's notation elsewhere in this version. M. 131, staff 1, upper voice, note 1 has no dot—an error; edition follows analogous m. 143; staff 2, beat 3 has eighth rest—an error as well as an inconsistency akin to that in m. 128. M. 137, staff 1, lower voice, note 1 is not stemmed with upper voice—an error; edition follows majority practice and analogous m. 149. M. 139, staff 1, dyads 2 and 4, lower voice is not stemmed with upper voice—edition follows majority practice elsewhere in this version.

## Appendix 6

*V. Final. Edition C', mm. 181–96.* To perform this version complete, play mm. 1–180 of edition *E* (noting the variants reported below), then the excerpt given in this Appendix.

Measures 1–180 in edition *C'* differ from edition *E* as follows. M. 31, staff 1, beat 1, the sixth part of the sextuplet is g"[-sharp]/b' eighth-note dyad instead of eighth rest; staff 3, note 1 is dotted—an error.

## Appendix 7

*V. Final. Edition D, mm. 181–95.* To perform this version complete, play mm. 1–180 of edition *E*, then the excerpt given in this Appendix.

M. 194, staff 2, top voice, note 1 (e' half note) has no dot—an error.

Measures 1–180 in edition *D* differ from edition *E* as follows. M. 31, staff 3, note 1 is dotted—an error.

# Widor's *Avant-propos*

Although it may not be customary to place a preface at the front of musical editions, I believe it is necessary to put one here in order to explain the character, the style, the procedures of registration, and the sign conventions of these eight symphonies.

Old instruments had almost no reed stops: two colors, white and black, foundation stops and mixture stops—that was their entire palette; moreover, each transition between this white and this black was abrupt and rough; the means of graduating the body of sound did not exist. Consequently, Bach and his contemporaries deemed it pointless to indicate registrations for their works—the mixture stops traditionally remaining appropriate to rapid movements, and the foundation stops to pieces of a more solemn pace.

The invention of the "swell box" dates back to just before the end of the eighteenth century. In a work published in 1772, the Dutchman Hess de Gouda expresses the admiration he felt upon hearing Handel, in London, coming to grips with the new device; some time later, in 1780, Abbé Vogler recommends the use of the "box" in the German manufacture of instruments. The idea gained ground, but without great artistic effect—for in spite of the most perspicacious efforts,* they did not succeed in going beyond the limits of a thirty-key manual and an insignificant number of registers.

It was necessary to wait until 1839 for the solution to the problem.

The honor for it redounds to French industry and the glory to Mr. A. Cavaillé-Coll. It is he who conceived the diverse wind pressures, the divided windchests, the pedal systems and the combination registers, he who applied for the first time Barker's pneumatic motors, created the family of harmonic stops, reformed and perfected the mechanics to such a point that each pipe—low or high, loud or soft—instantly obeys the touch of the finger, the keys becoming as light as those of a piano—the resistances being suppressed, rendering the combination of [all] the forces of the instrument practical. From this result: the possibility of confining an entire division in a sonorous prison—opened or closed at will—the freedom of mixing timbres, the means of intensifying them or gradually tempering them, the freedom of tempos, the sureness of attacks, the balance of contrasts, and, finally, a whole blossoming of wonderful colors—a rich palette of the most diverse shades: harmonic flutes, gambas, bassoons, English horns, trumpets, celestes, flue stops and reed stops of a quality and variety unknown before.

The modern organ is essentially symphonic. The new instrument requires a new language, an ideal other than scholastic polyphony. It is no longer the Bach of the fugue whom we invoke but the heartrending melodist, the preeminently expressive master of the Preludes, the Magnificat, the B-minor Mass, the cantatas, and the *St. Matthew Passion*.

But this "expressiveness" of the new instrument can only be subjective; it arises from mechanical means and cannot have spontaneity. While the stringed and wind instruments of the orchestra, the piano, and voices reign only by naturalness of accent and unexpectedness of attack, the organ, clothed in its primordial majesty, speaks as a philosopher: alone among all, it can put forth the same volume of sound indefinitely and thus inspire the religious idea of the infinite. Surprises and accents are not natural to it; they are lent to it, they are accents by adoption. It is clear that their use requires tact and discernment. It is also clear to what extent the organ symphony differs from the orchestral symphony. No confusion is to be feared. One will never write indiscriminately for the orchestra or for the organ, but henceforth one will have to exercise the same care with the combination of timbres in an organ composition as in an orchestral work.

Rhythm itself must come under the influence of modern trends: it must lend itself to a sort of elasticity of the measure, all the while preserving its rights. It must allow the musical phrase to punctuate its paragraphs and breathe when necessary, provided that it hold [the phrase] by the bit and that [the phrase] march to its step. Without rhythm, without this constant manifestation of the will returning periodically to the strong beat, the performer will not be listened to. How often the composer hesitates and abstains at the moment of writing on his score the *poco ritenuto* that he has in his thought! He does not dare, from fear that the exaggeration of the performer may weaken or break the flow of the piece. The indication is left out. We do not have the graphic means for emphasizing the end of a period, or reinforcing a chord by a type of pause of unnoticeable duration. Isn't it a great shame, especially since the organ is an instrument that draws all of its effect from time values?

As to terminology, the system indicating the disposition of timbres—usage having established nothing as yet—it seemed practical to me to note the manual and pedal registration at the head of each piece; to apportion by tone colors, rather than an exact nomenclature of stops, the intensity of the sonorities of the same family; to designate the manuals by their abbreviations (two or

---

*Experiments of Sébastien Erard: Organ constructed in 1826 for the chapel of the Legion of Honor at St.-Denis—Exposition at the Louvre in 1827.

more initials juxtaposed signifying the coupling of two or more manuals); to assume the reed stops always prepared; and finally to reserve *fff* for the full power of the organ, without having to mention the introduction of the ventil (Anches) pedals. In the combination **GR** [Grand-orgue, Récit], the crescendo applies only to the Récit, unless this crescendo leads to the *fff*, in which case all the forces of the instrument must enter little by little in order, flues and reeds.

It is unnecessary, I believe, to implore the same precision, the same coordination of the feet and hands in leaving a keyboard as in attacking it, and to protest against all carrying-over of the pedal after the time, an old-fashioned custom that has happily almost disappeared.

With the consummate musicians of today, the insufficiencies and shortcomings in musical notation become less worrisome; the composer is more certain of seeing his intentions understood and his implications perceived. Between him and the performer is a steadfast collaboration, which the growing number of virtuosos will render more intimate and fruitful every day.

Ch. M. W.

Plate 1. Symphonie III: V. Final, edition *C*, copy *Schw*1–3, page 94, systems 4 and 5, comprising measures 26–31. The last two measures of this passage are written in ink in Widor's hand on a piece of manuscript paper glued to the page. The hastily written natural in measure 31, staff 1 before the g″ on beat 3 (it resembles an upstem for the preceding e″ eighth note and a sixteenth rest) is in pencil (perhaps added by Widor; the absence of a sharp on g′ in mm. 30–31 may be due to Widor's notational habits rather than to oversight). Directly below in staff 2 the rests are misaligned leftward by one eighth note, there is one eighth rest too many, and the directive **GPR** is missing from note 2; in staff 3 the directive indicating Pédale couplers is missing and the C half note lacks a dot. Errors apart, the paste-over gives a slightly different reading from that which appears in edition *C'* (see Critical Commentary, reports for "V. Final," m. 31, and for "Appendix 6," m. 31).

Courtesy Maison Schweitzer, Gunsbach, France

Symphonie III in E Minor

Grand orgue: Fonds 16', 8', 4'
Positif: Fonds 8'
Récit: Anches 16', 8', 4' et Clarinette alternativement
Pédale: Fonds 32', 16', 8', 4'

# [I] Prélude

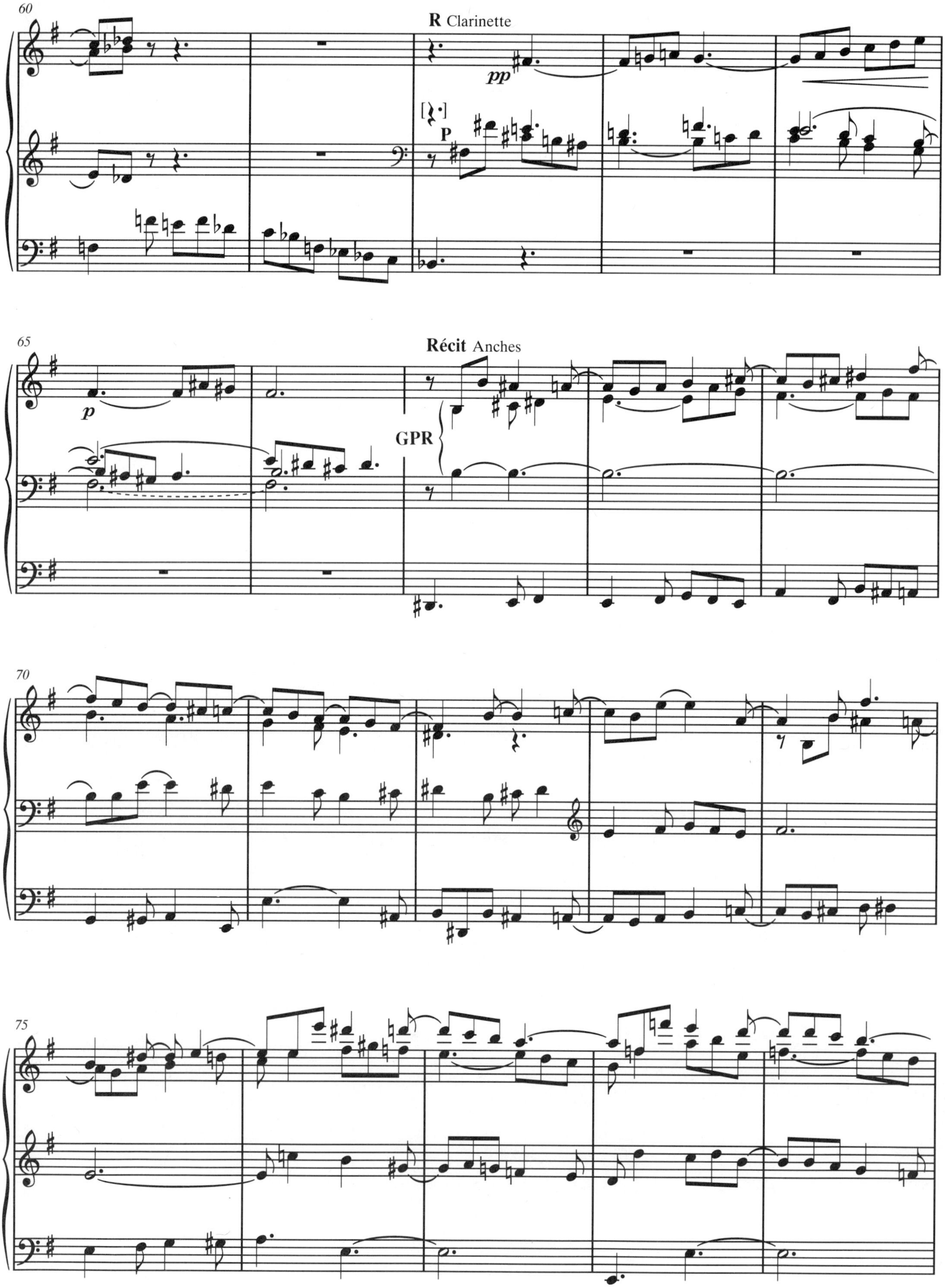
60
R Clarinette
pp
P
65
Récit Anches
p
GPR
70
75

Grand orgue: Flûte 8'
Positif: Diapason [8'] et Principal [8']
Récit: Hautbois 8'
Pédale: Flûte 8'

# II. Minuetto

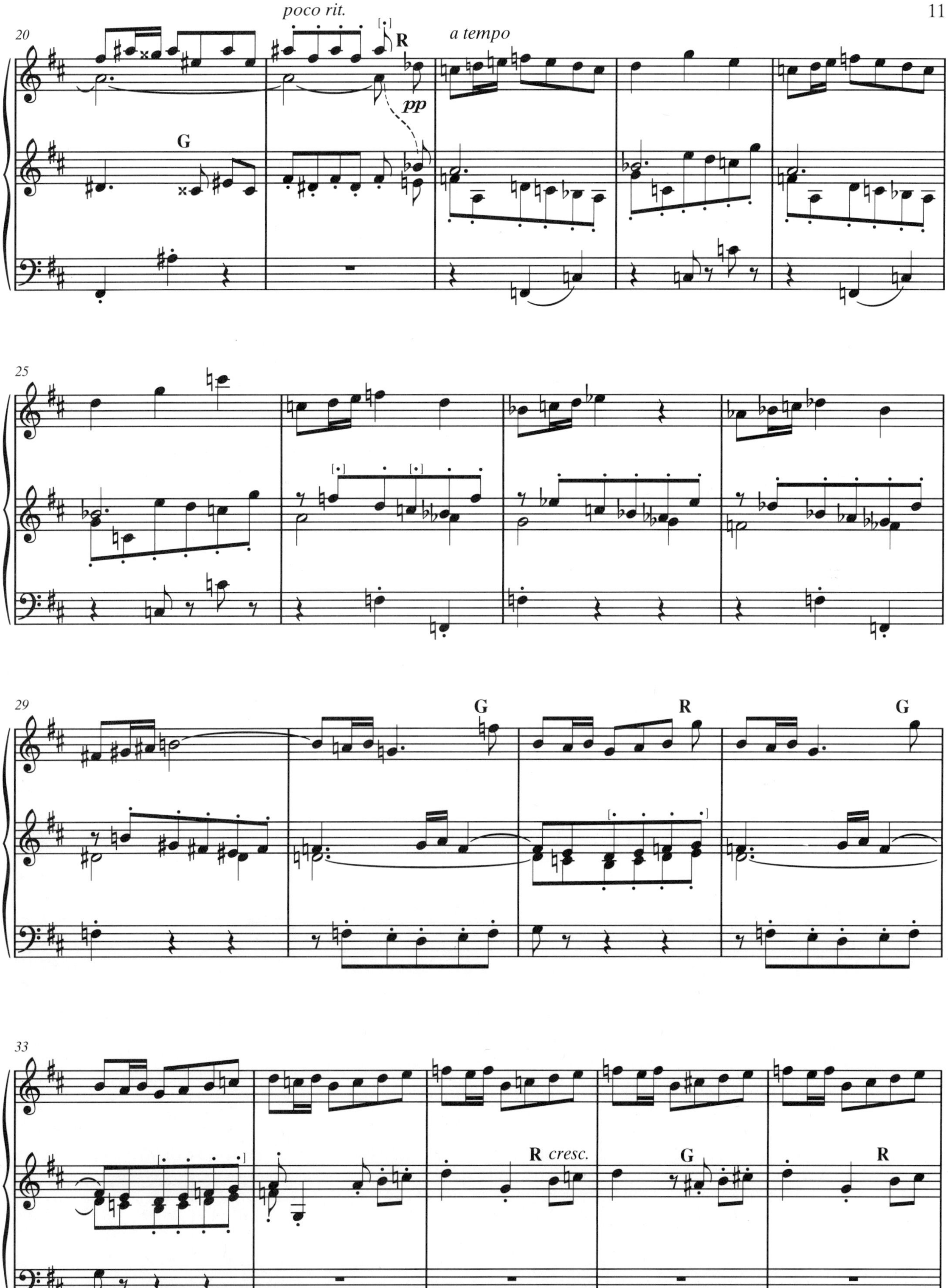
20
poco rit.
a tempo
R
pp
G
25
29
G
R
G
33
R cresc.
G
R

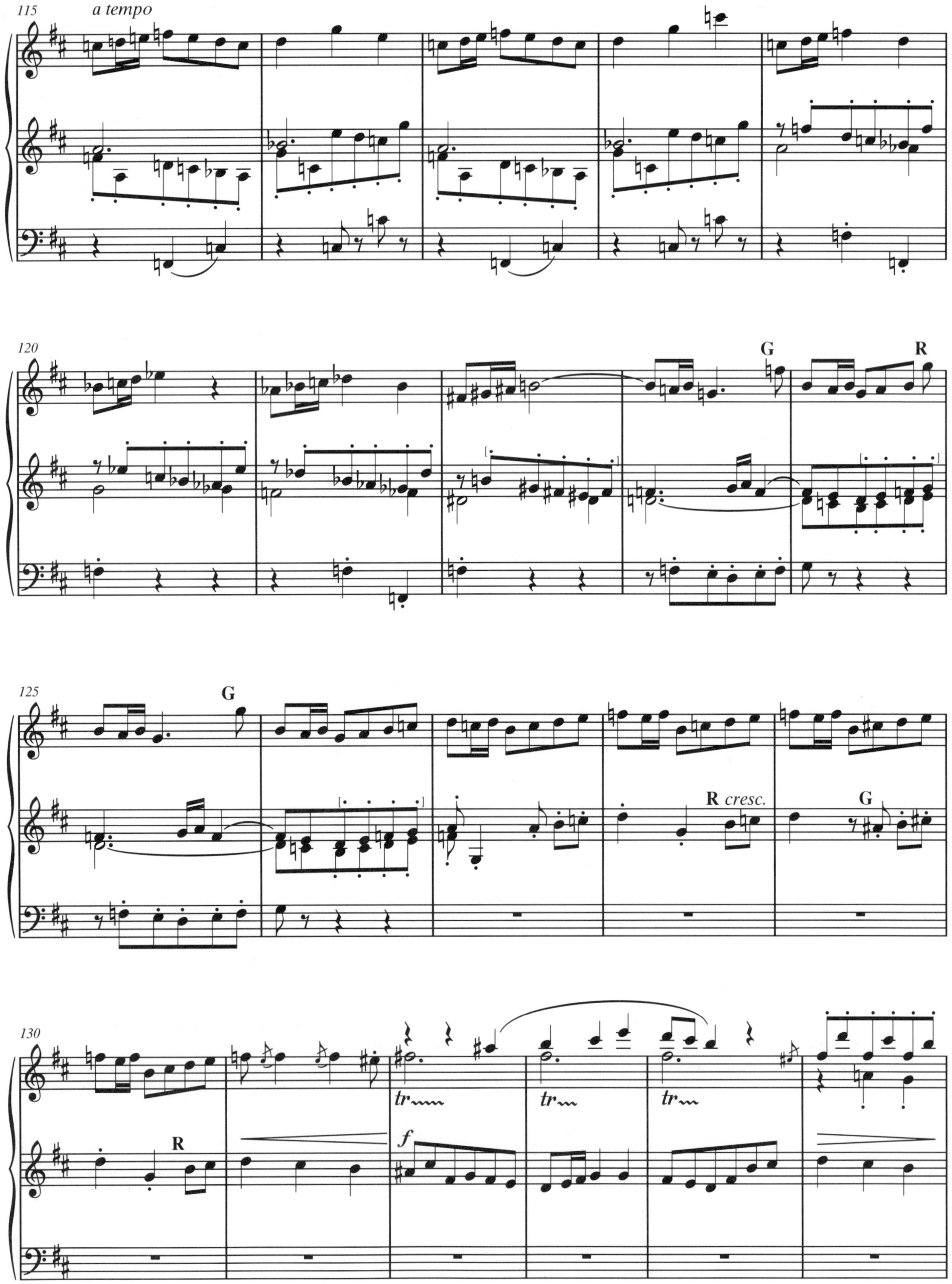
115
a tempo
120
G
R
125
G
R cresc.
G
130
R
tr
f
tr
tr

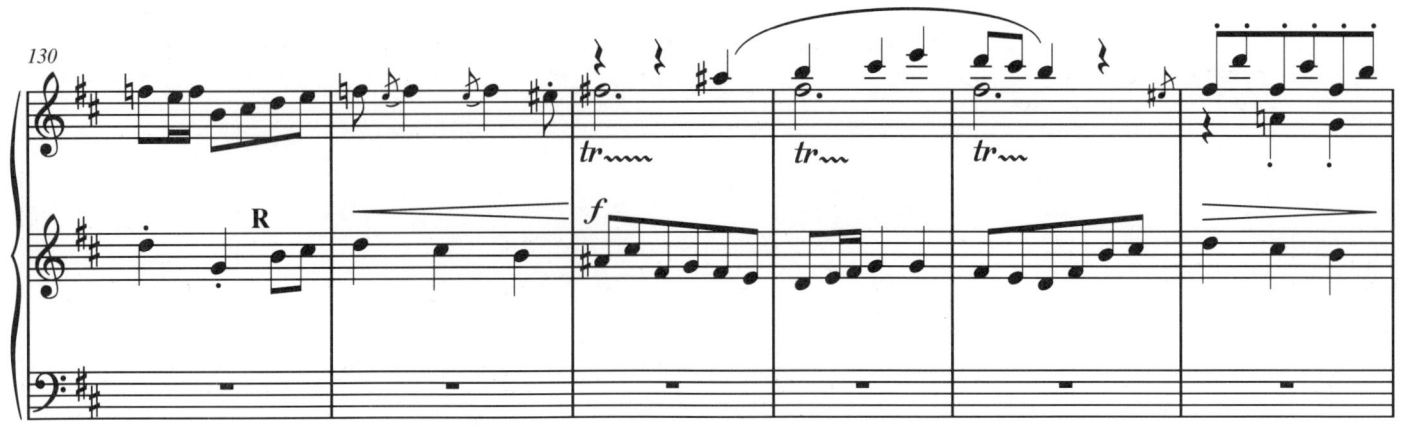

17

# III. Marcia

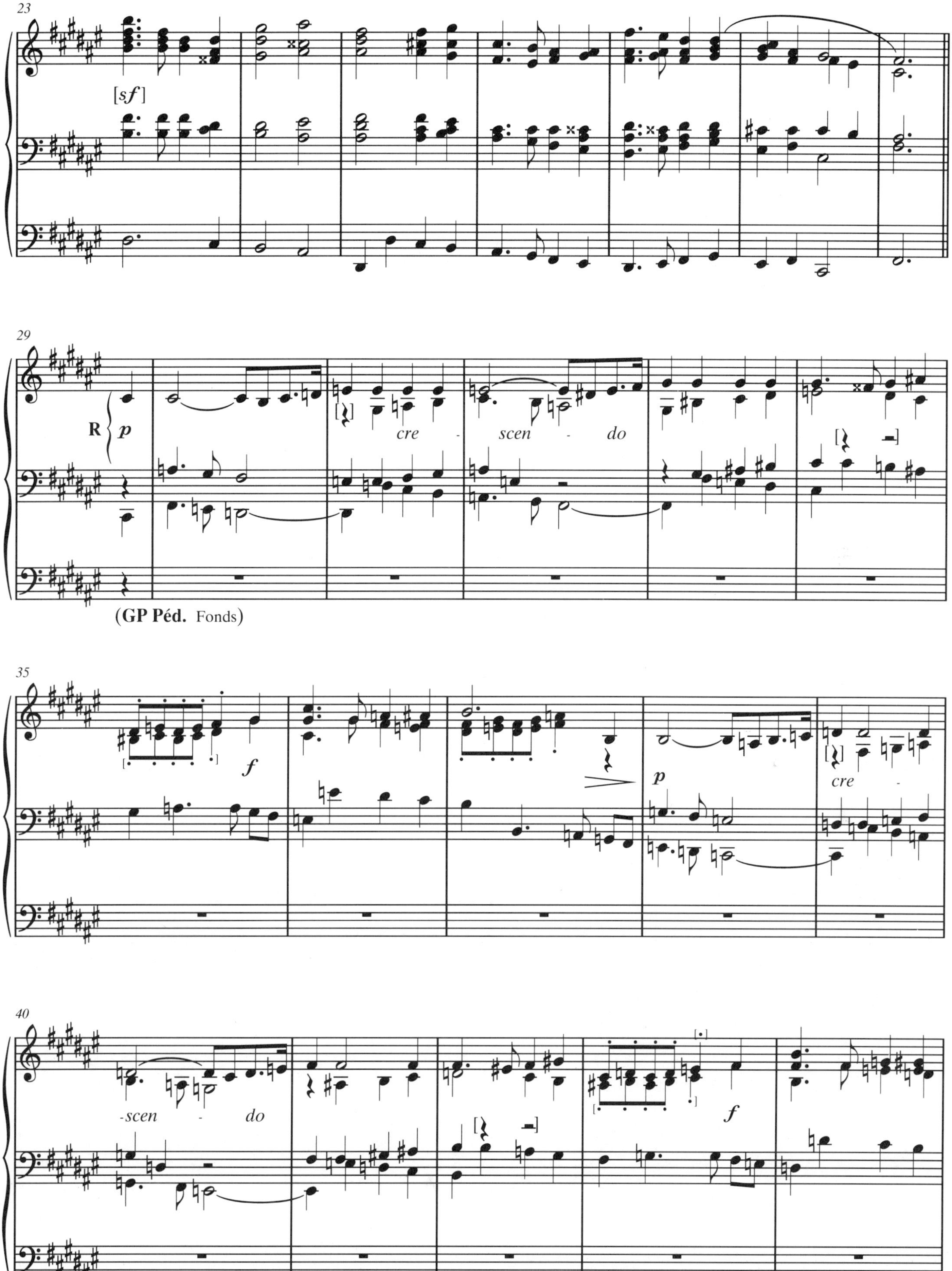
23
[sf]
29
R
p
cre - scen - do
(GP Péd. Fonds)
35
f
p
cre -
40
-scen - do
f

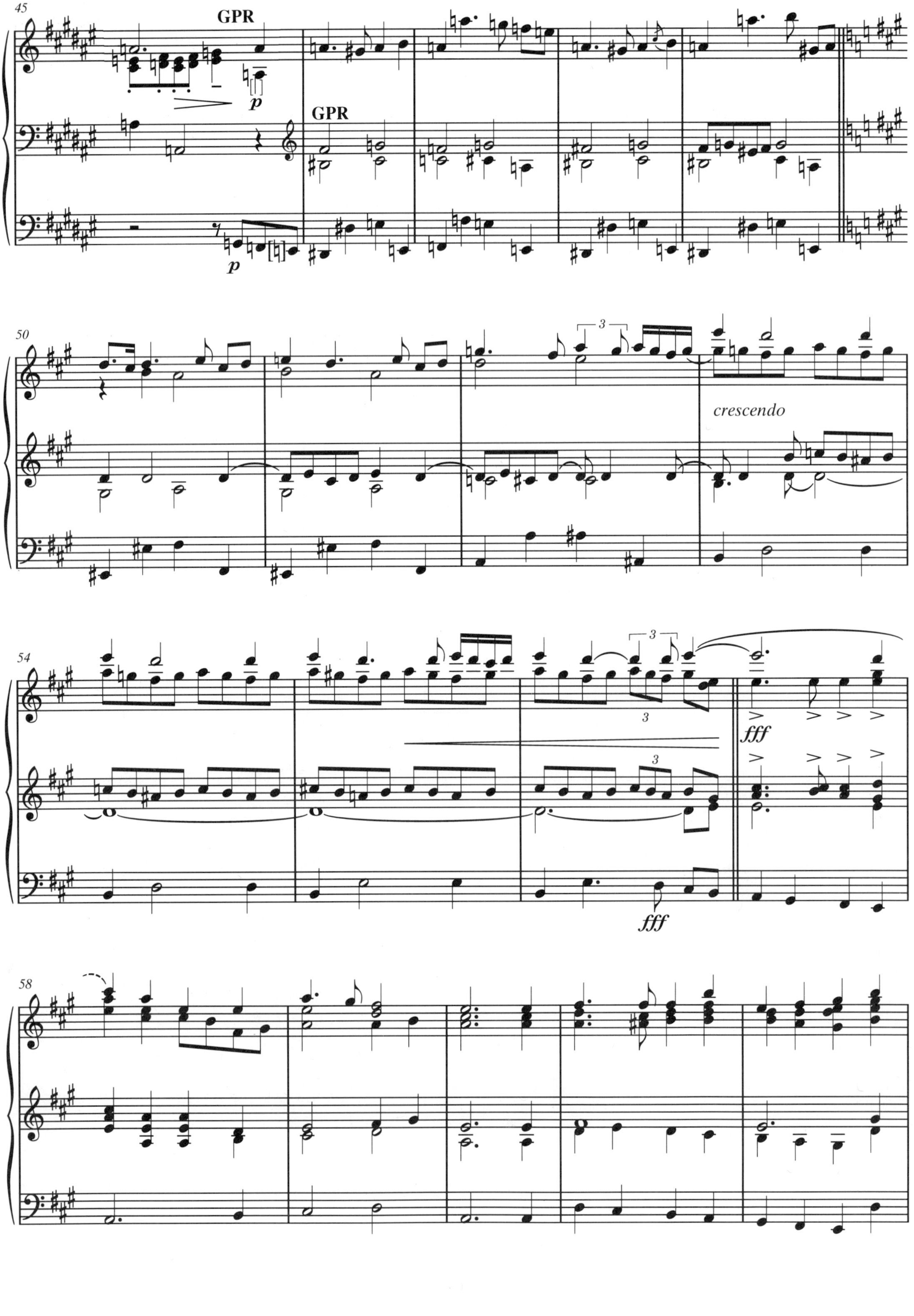
45
GPR
p
GPR
p
50
crescendo
54
fff
fff
58

21

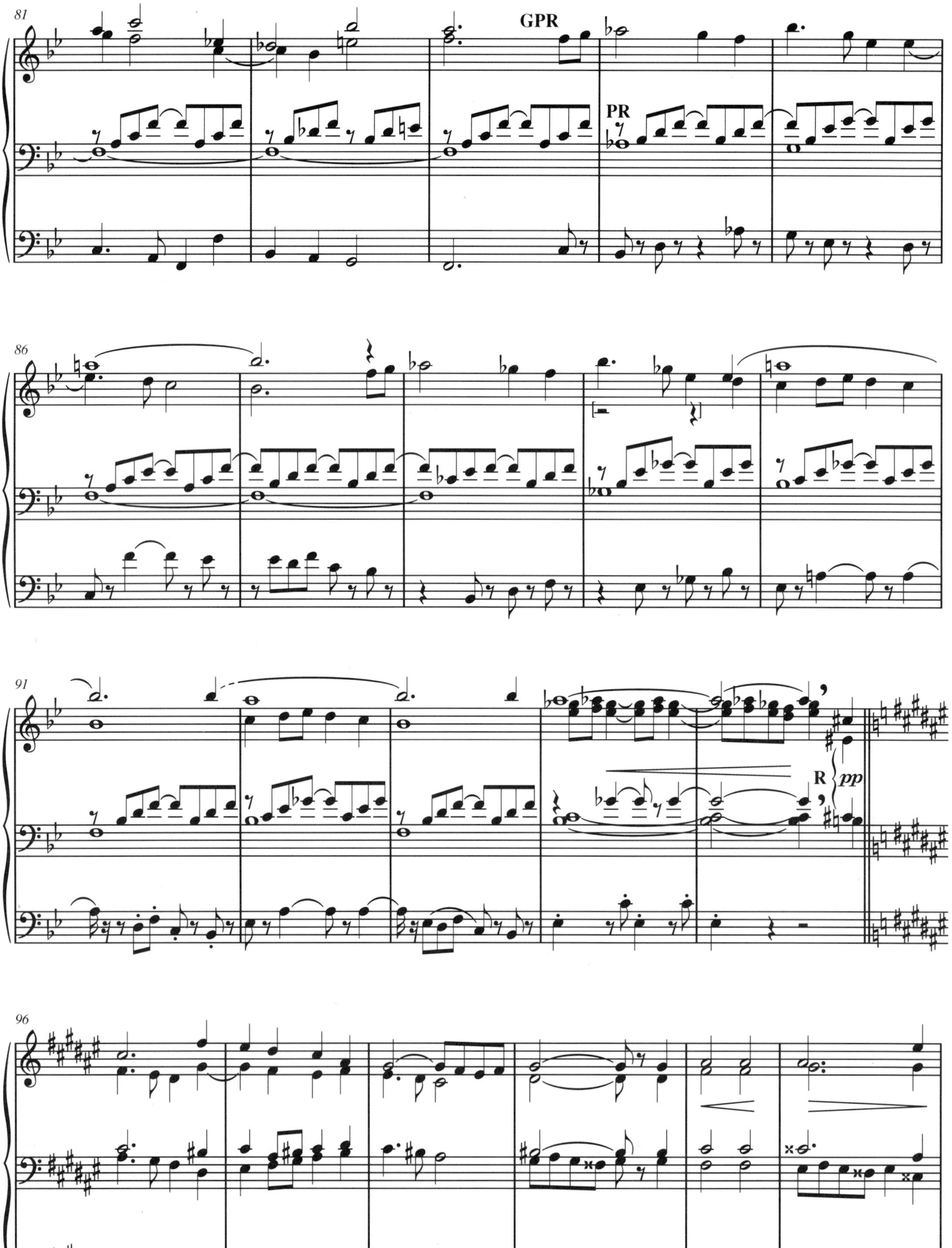
81
GPR
PR
86
91
R
pp
96

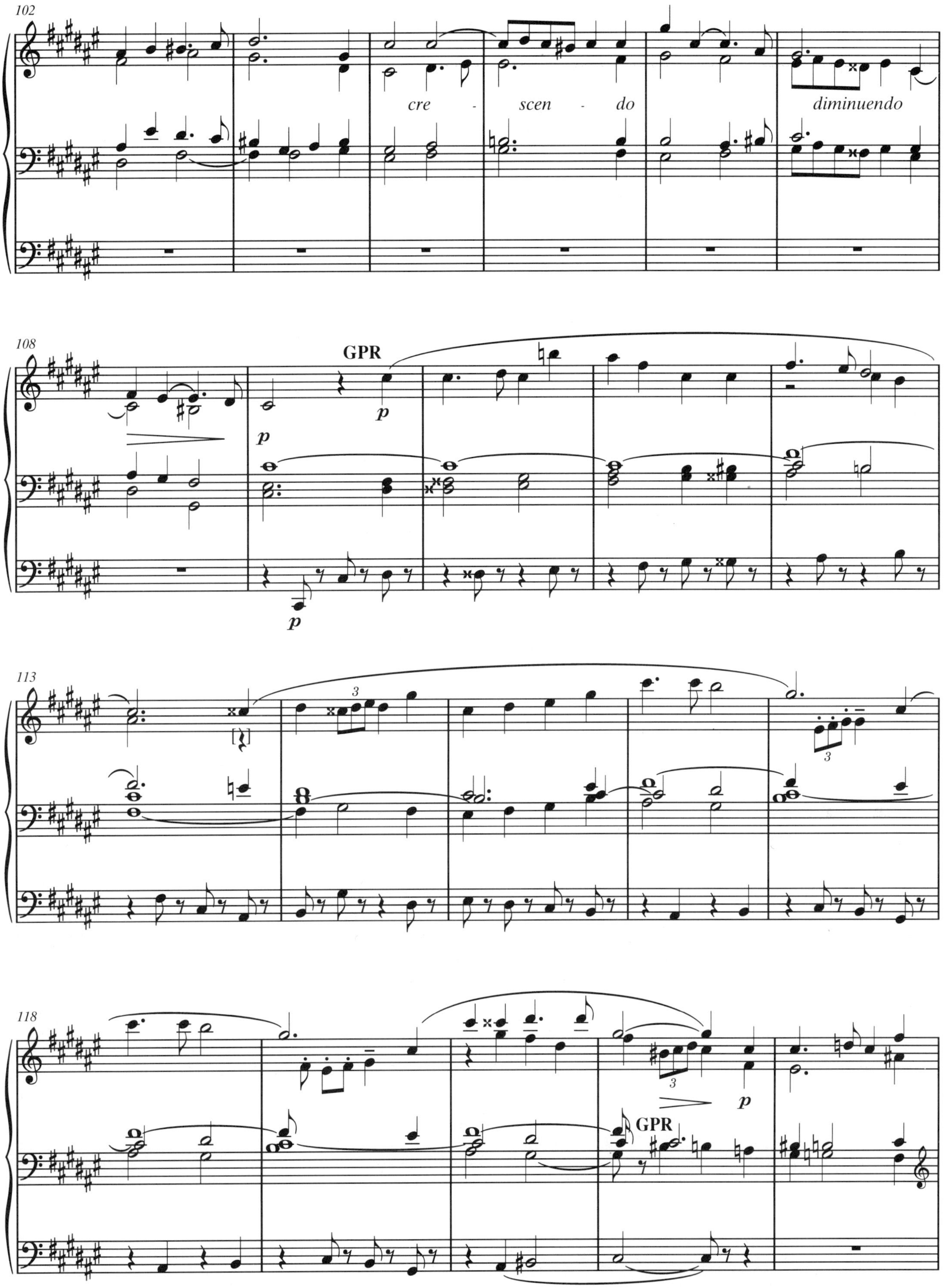
102
cre - scen - do
diminuendo
108
GPR
p
p
p
113
3
3
118
3
p
GPR

24

25

*poco meno vivo e sostenuto*

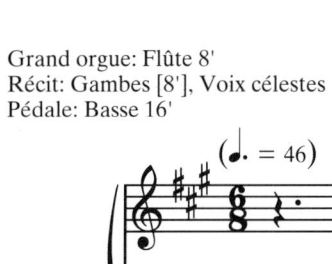

Grand orgue: Flûte 8'
Récit: Gambes [8'], Voix célestes
Pédale: Basse 16'

# IV. Adagio

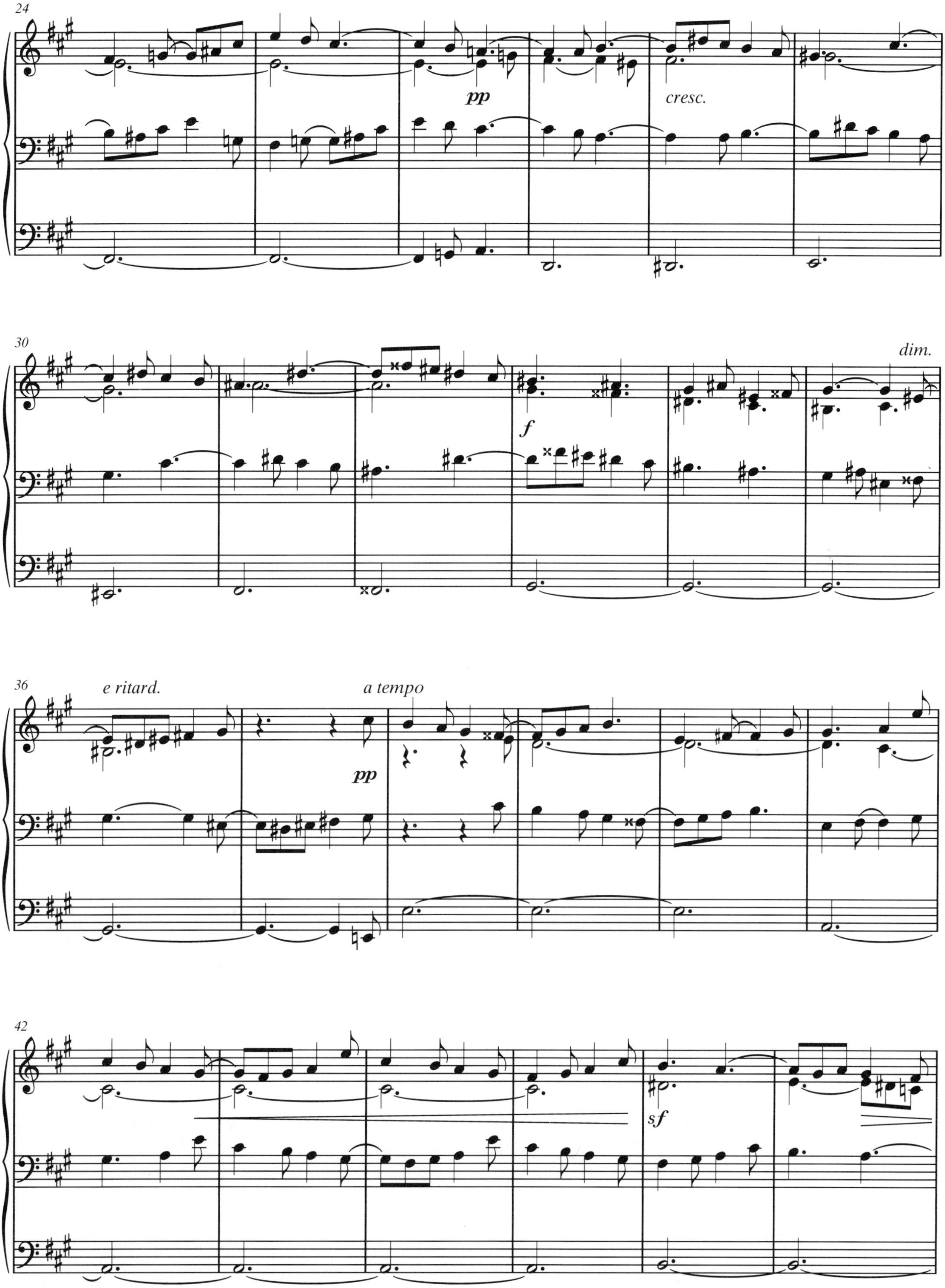
24
pp
cresc.
30
dim.
f
36
e ritard.
a tempo
pp
42
sf

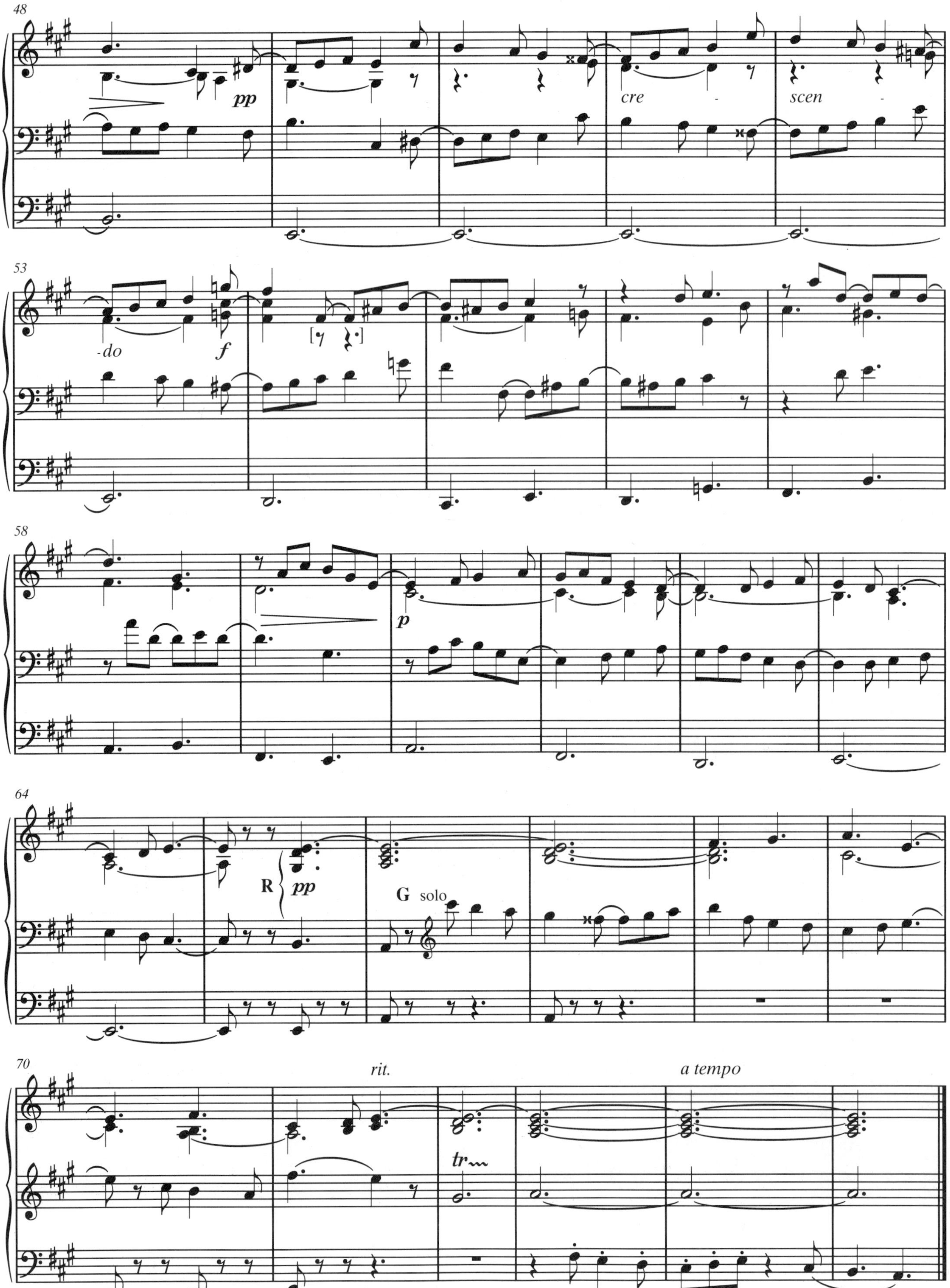
48
pp
cre - scen - do
f
53
58
p
64
R
pp
G solo
70
rit.
a tempo
tr

Grand orgue: Fonds 16', 8', 4'
Positif: Fonds 8', 4'
Récit: Fonds et Anches 16', 8', 4'
Pédale: Fonds 16', 8', 4'

# V. Final

**Allegro molto**

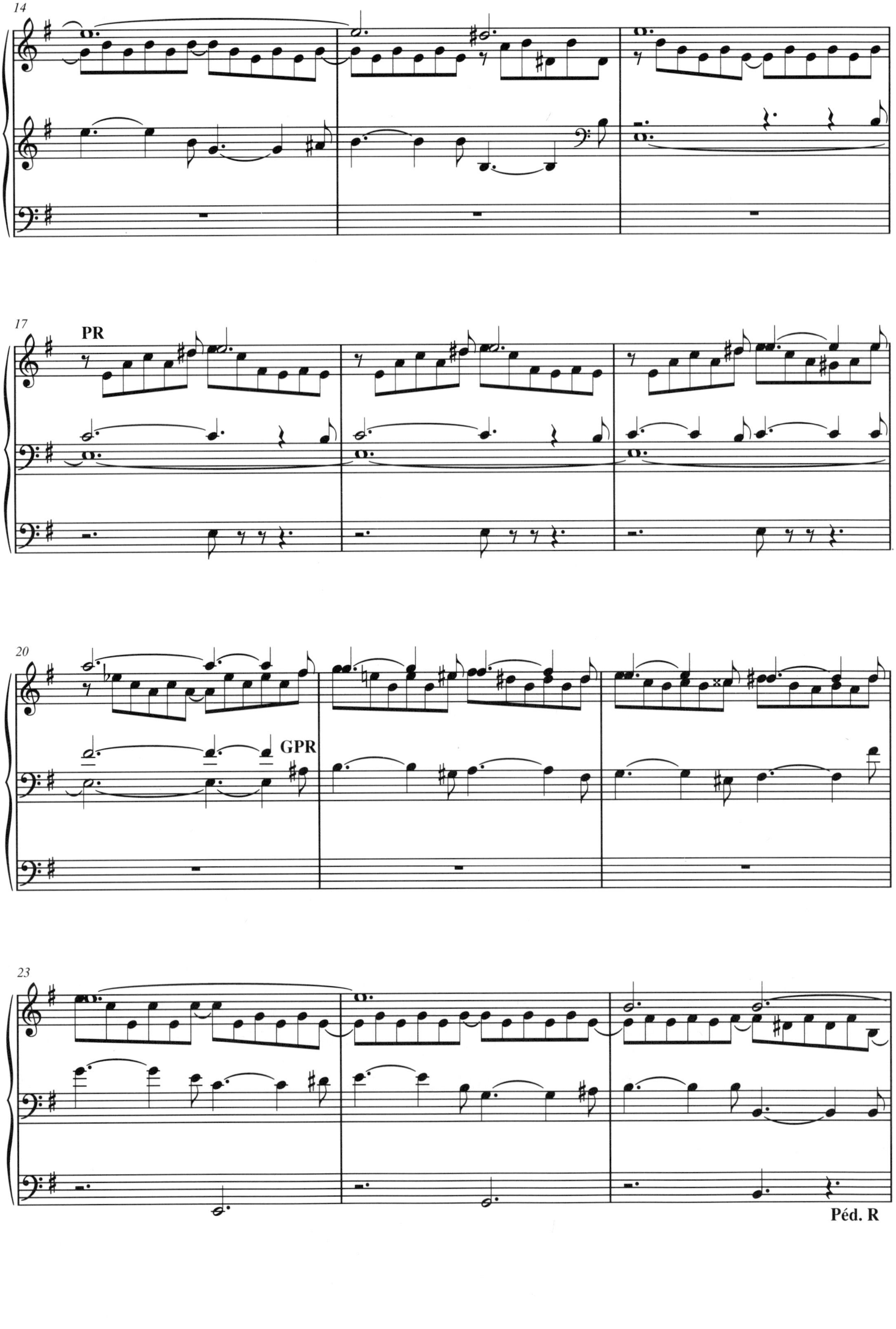
14
17
PR
20
GPR
23
Péd. R

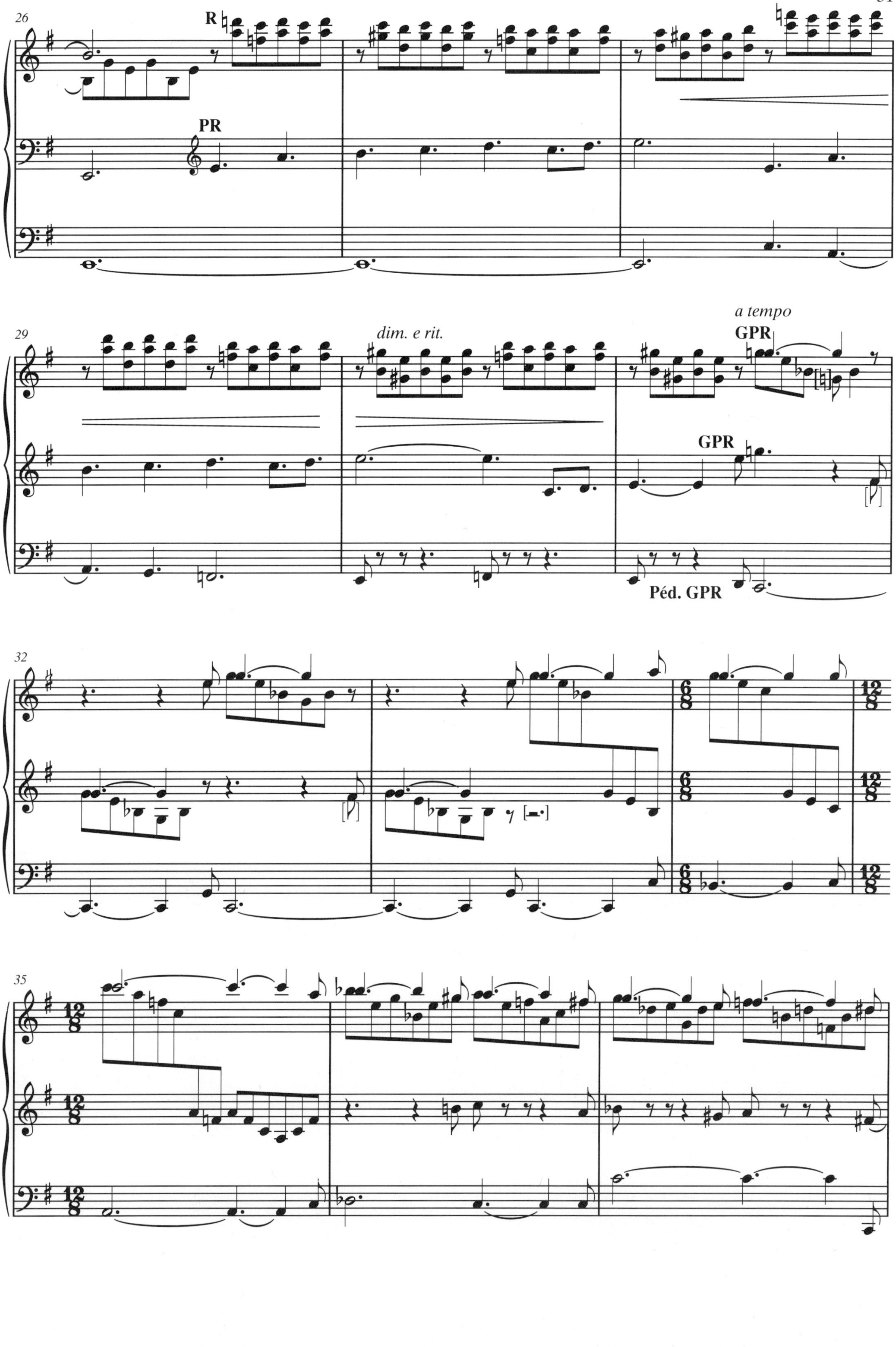
26
R
PR
29
dim. e rit.
a tempo
GPR
GPR
Péd. GPR
32
35

32

33

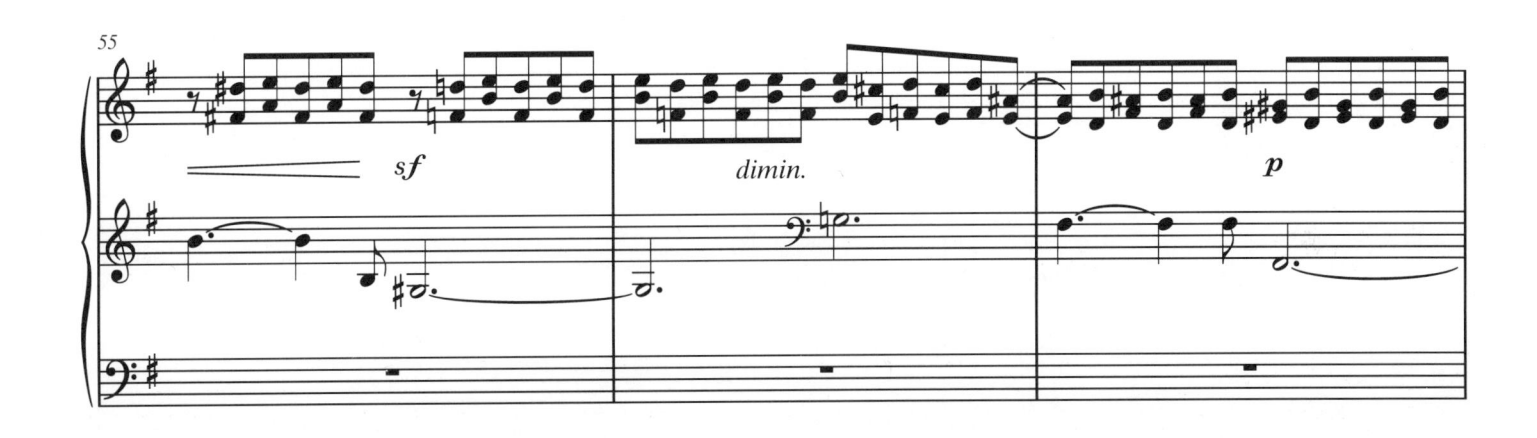

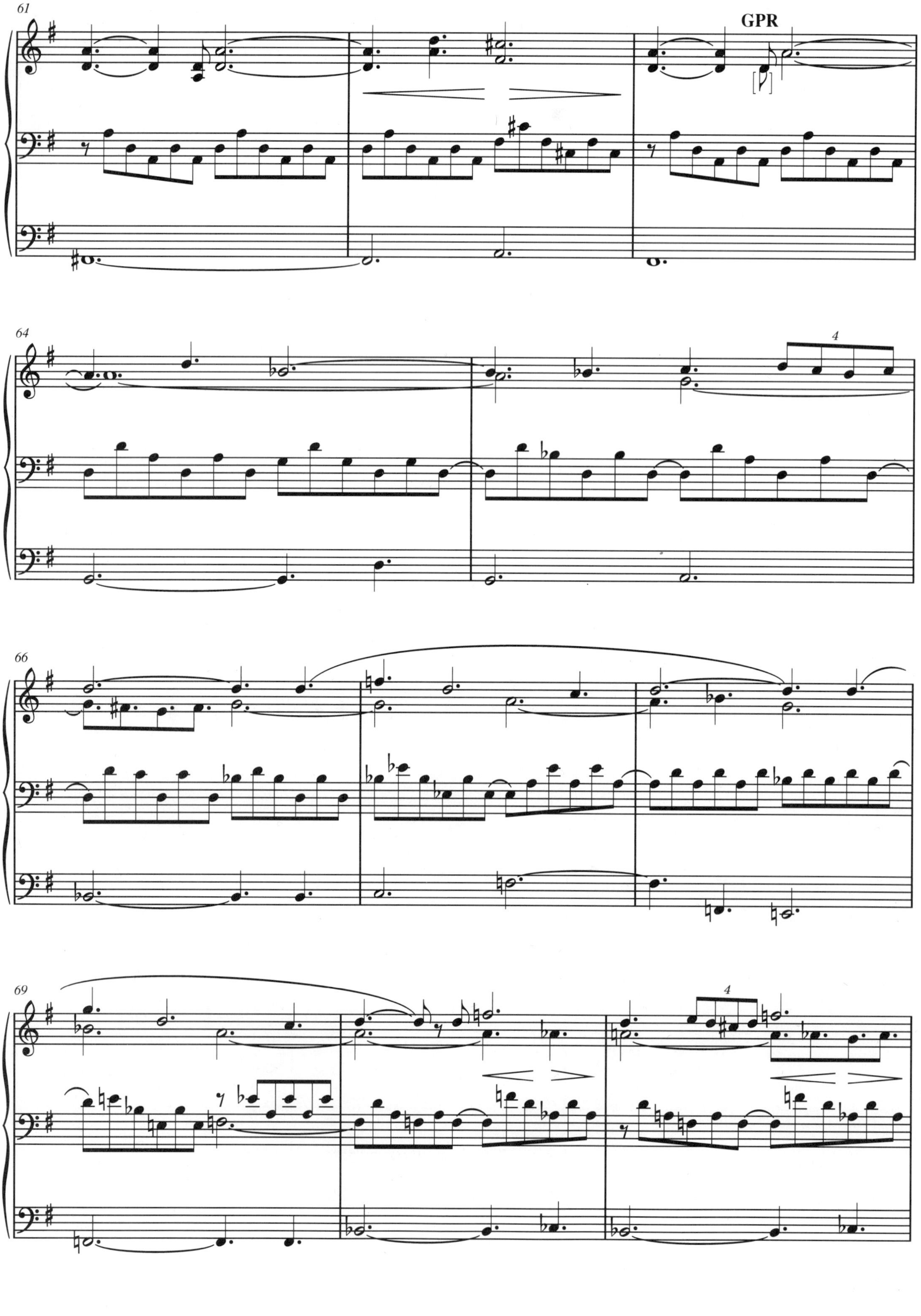
GPR

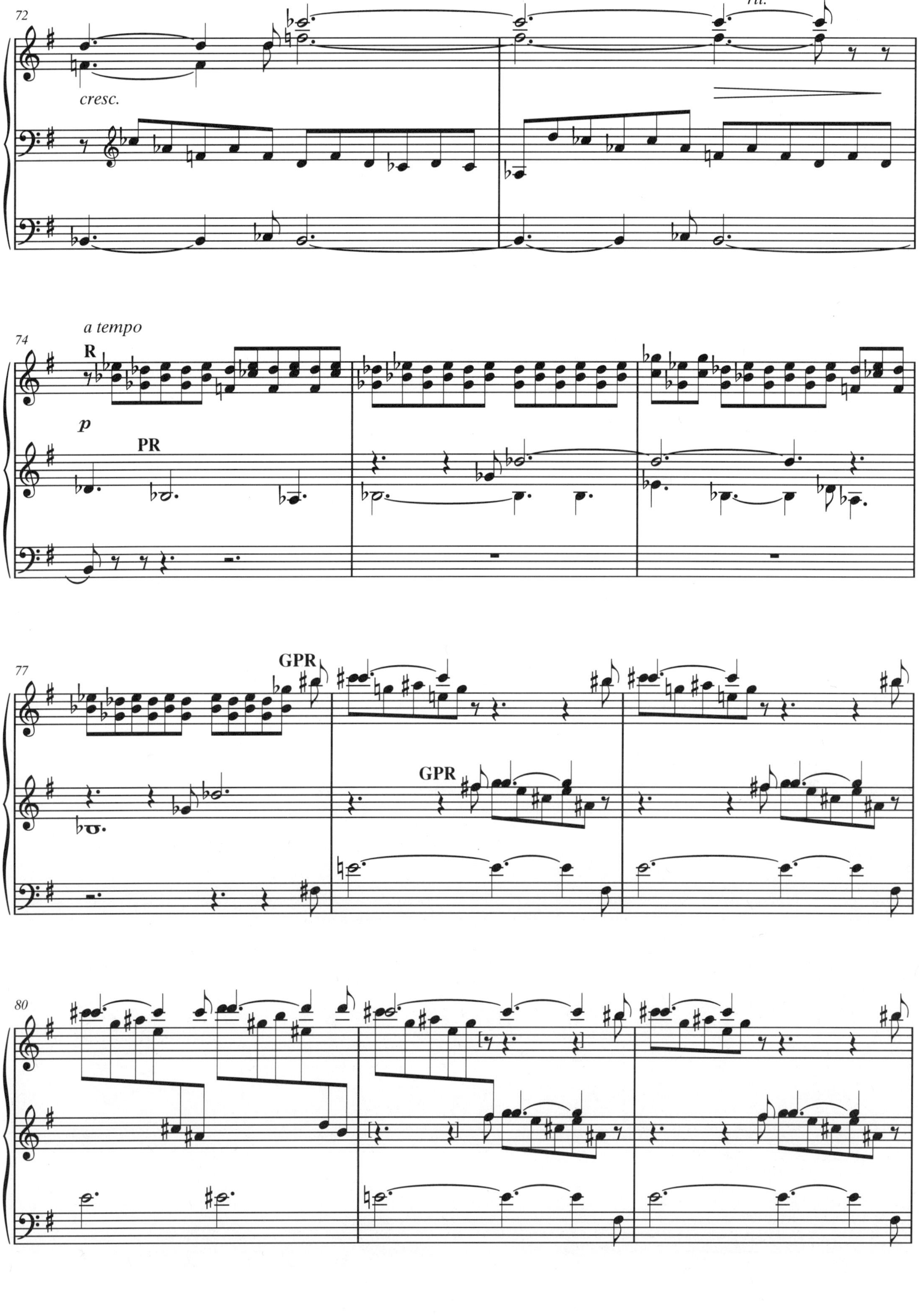
72
rit.
cresc.
74
a tempo
R
p
PR
77
GPR
GPR
80

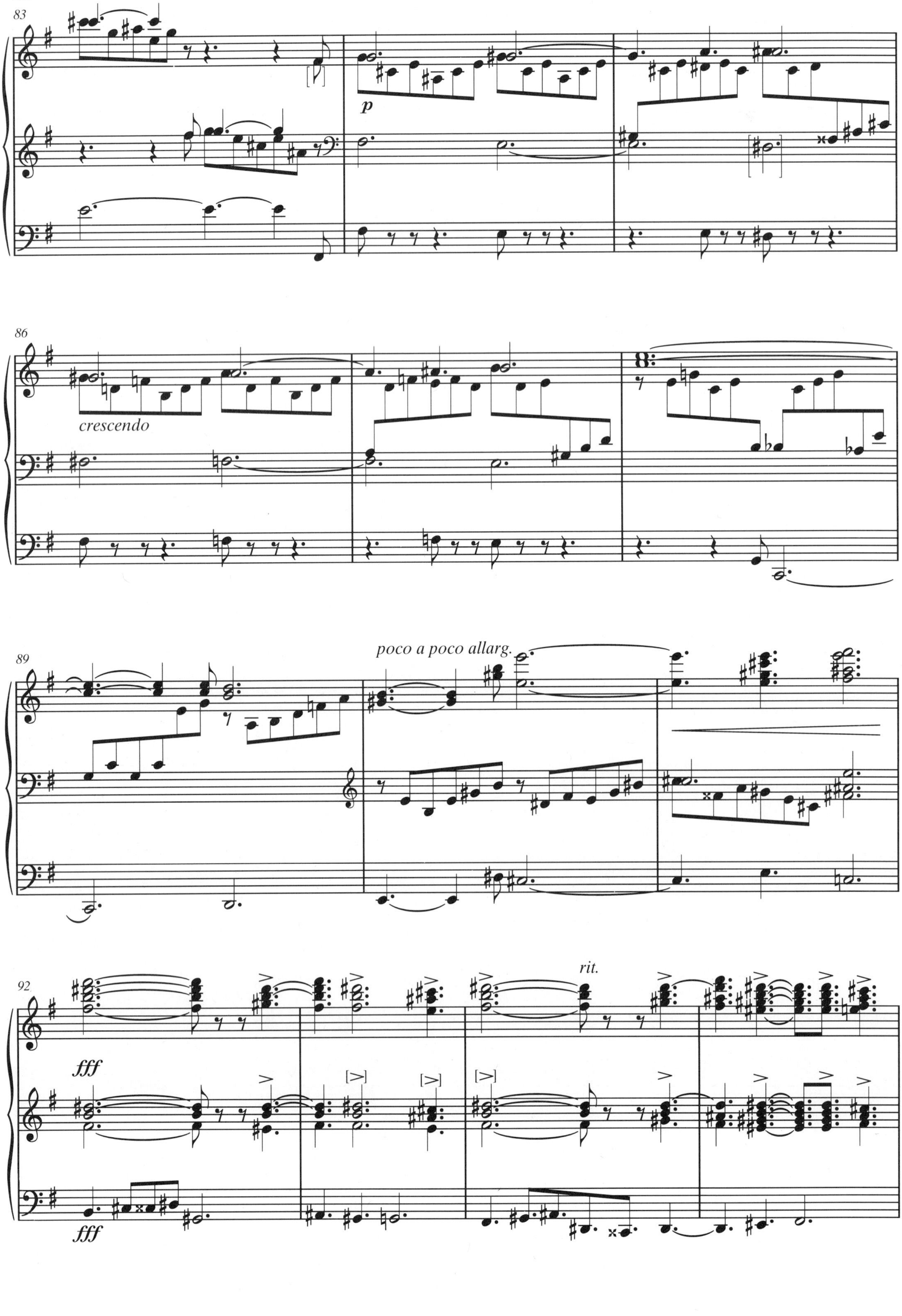
83
p
86
crescendo
89
poco a poco allarg.
92
fff
fff
rit.

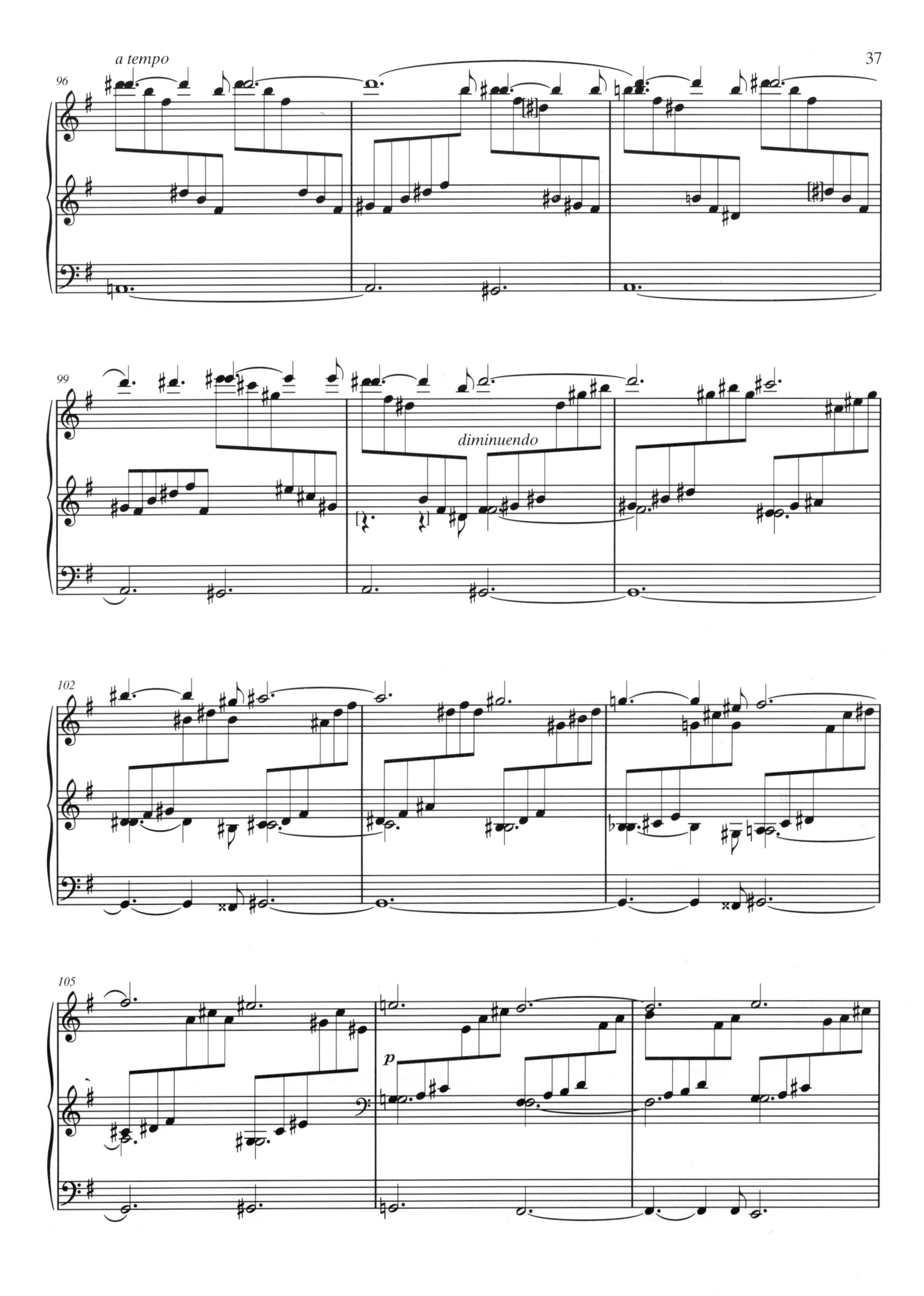
a tempo
96
99
diminuendo
102
105
p

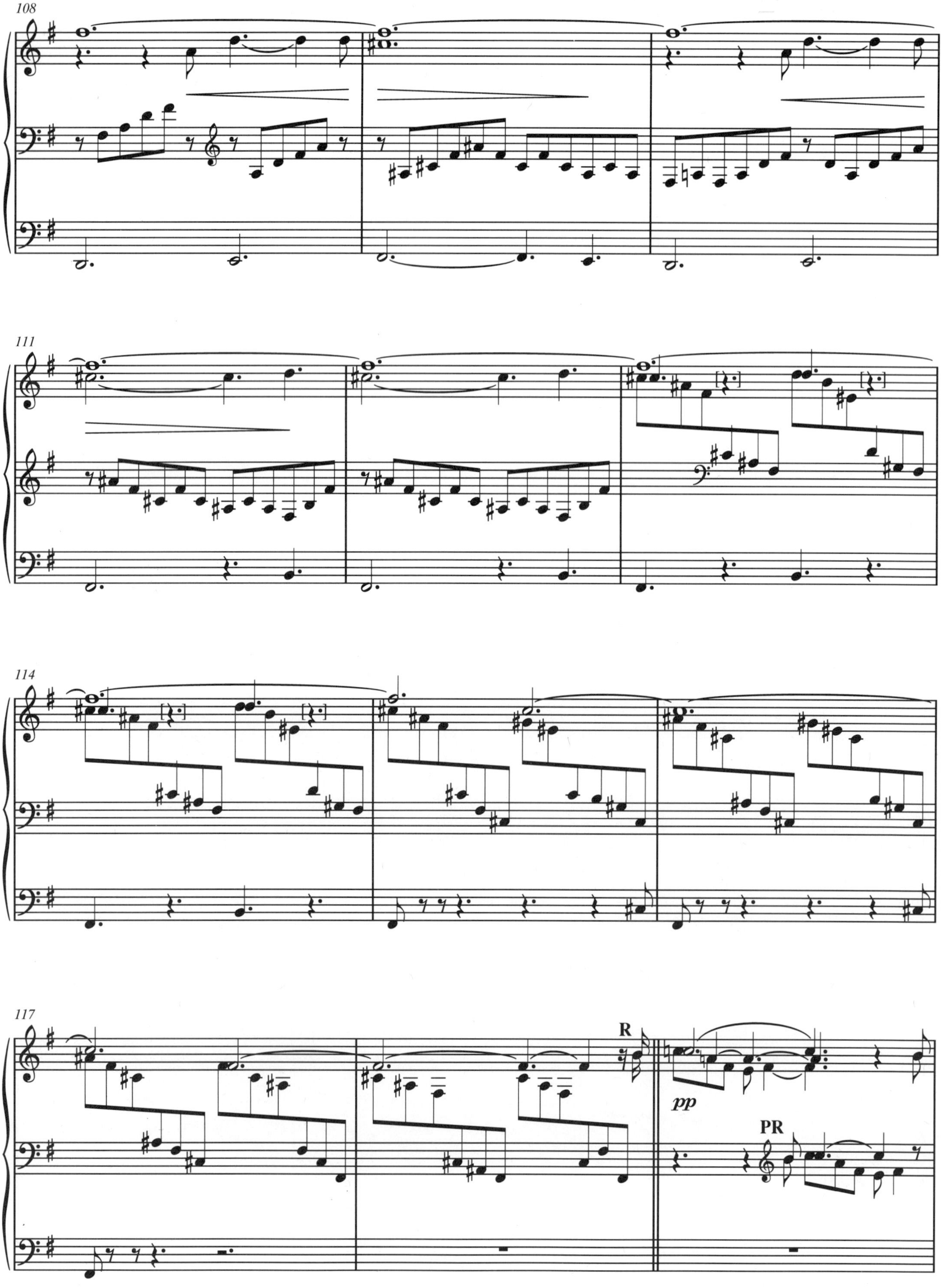
108
111
114
117
R
PR
pp

39

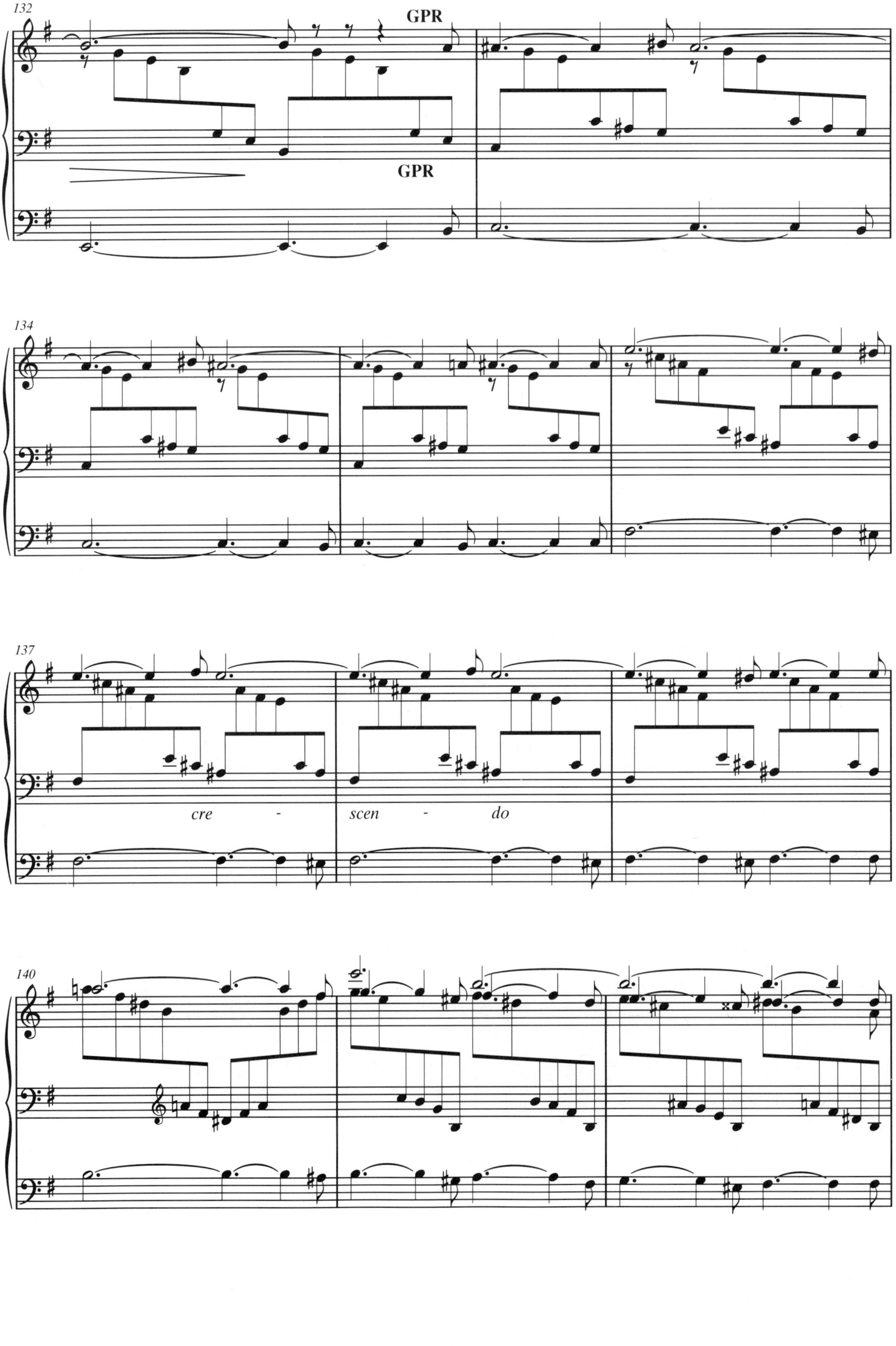
132
GPR
GPR
134
137
cre - scen - do
140

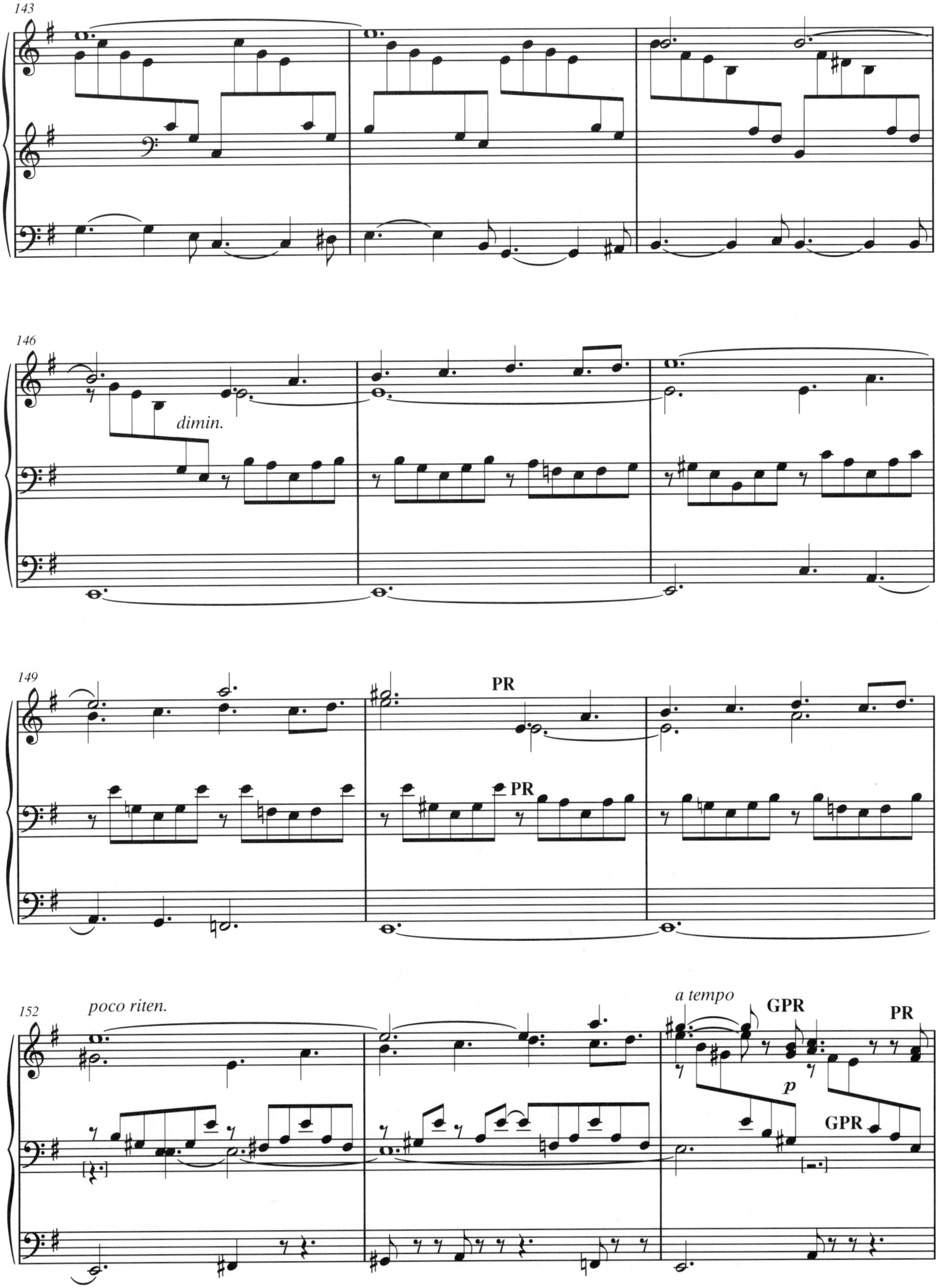
143
146
dimin.
149
PR
PR
152
poco riten.
a tempo
GPR
PR
p
GPR

42

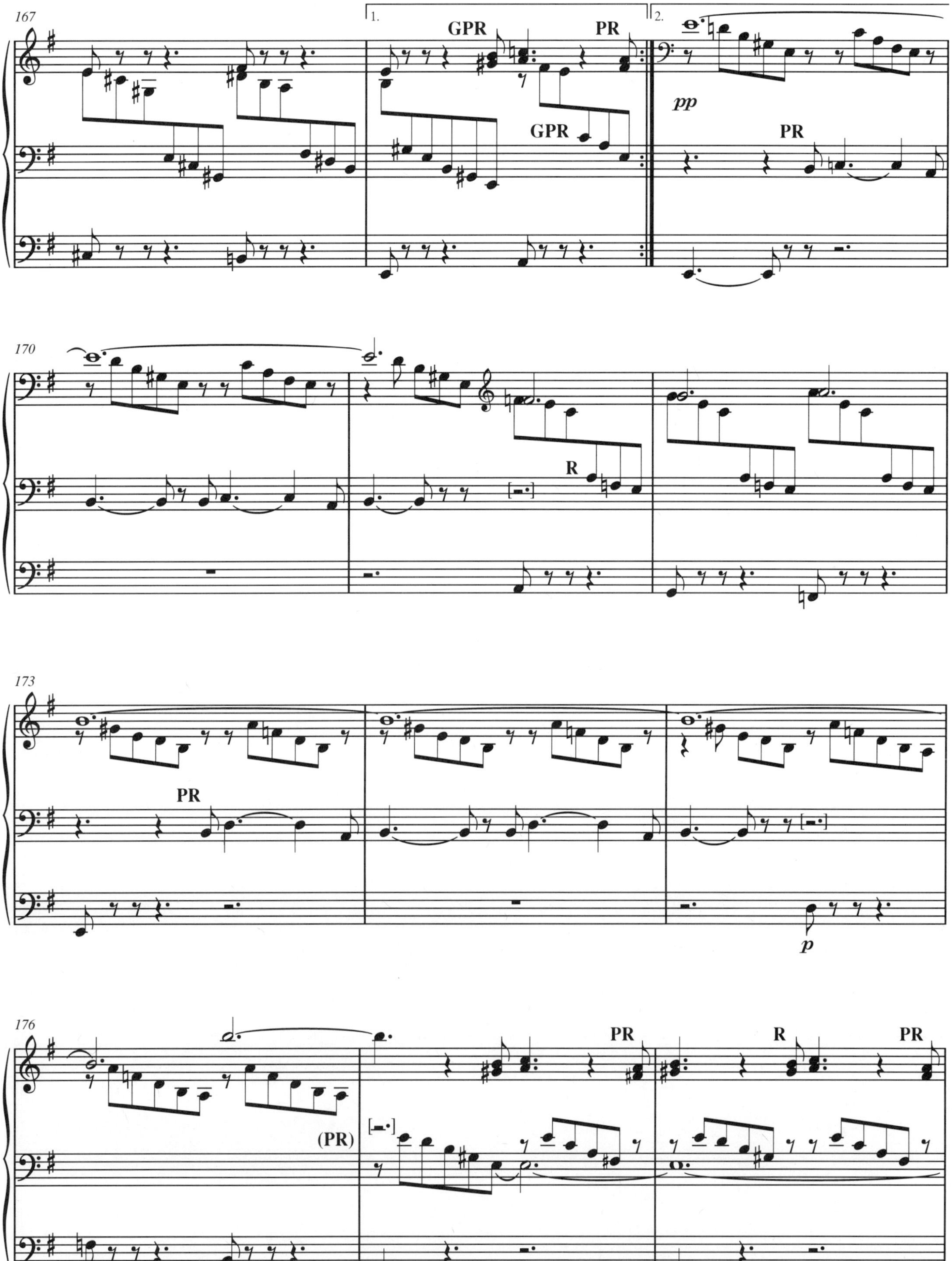
167
1.
2.
GPR
PR
GPR
PR
pp
170
R
173
PR
p
176
(PR)
PR
R
PR

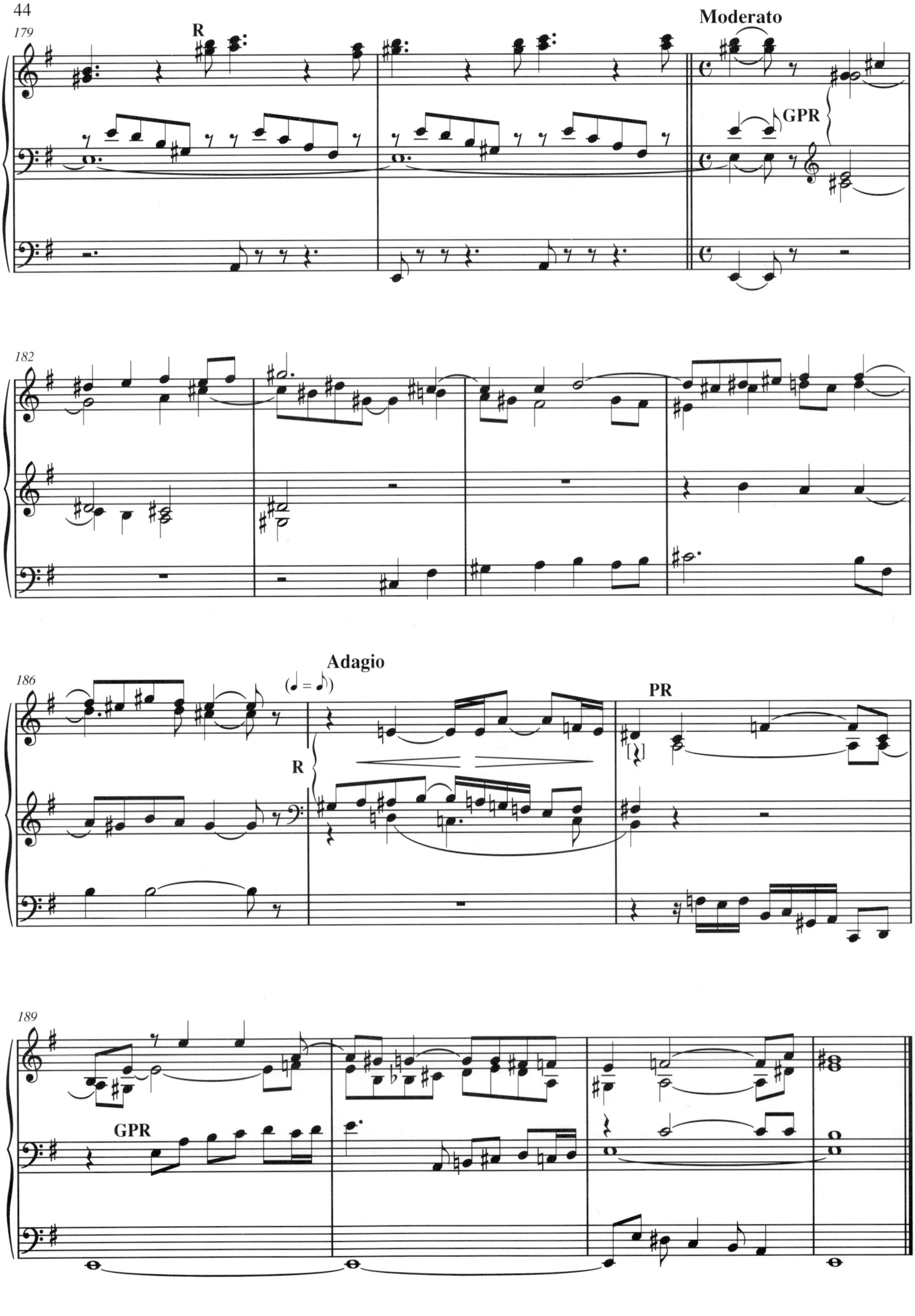
179
R
Moderato
GPR
182
186
Adagio
(♩ = ♪)
R
PR
189
GPR

# Appendix 1
# [III] Marcia

Version *A/A′*

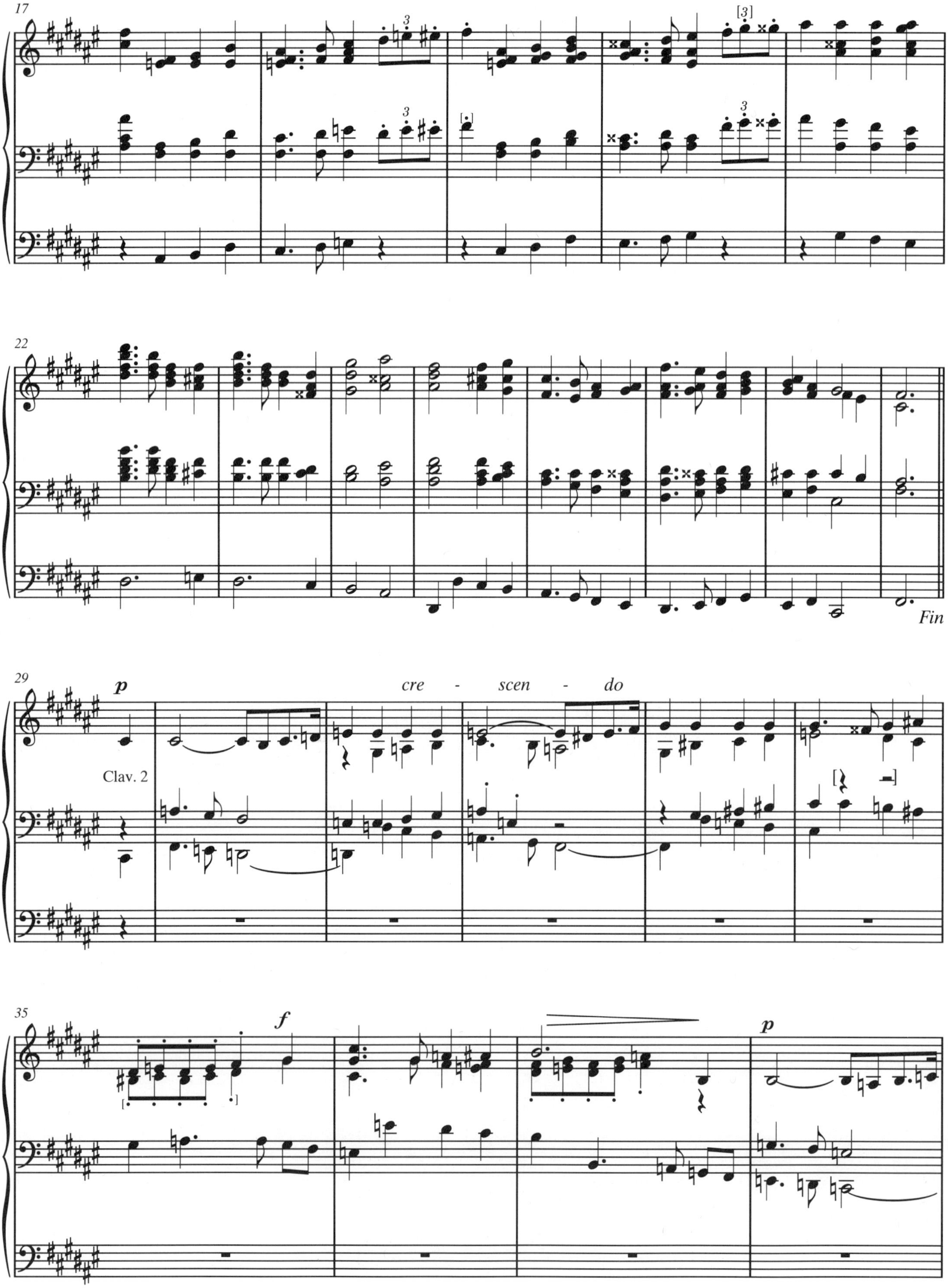
17
22
Fin
29
p
cre - scen - do
Clav. 2
35
f
p

47

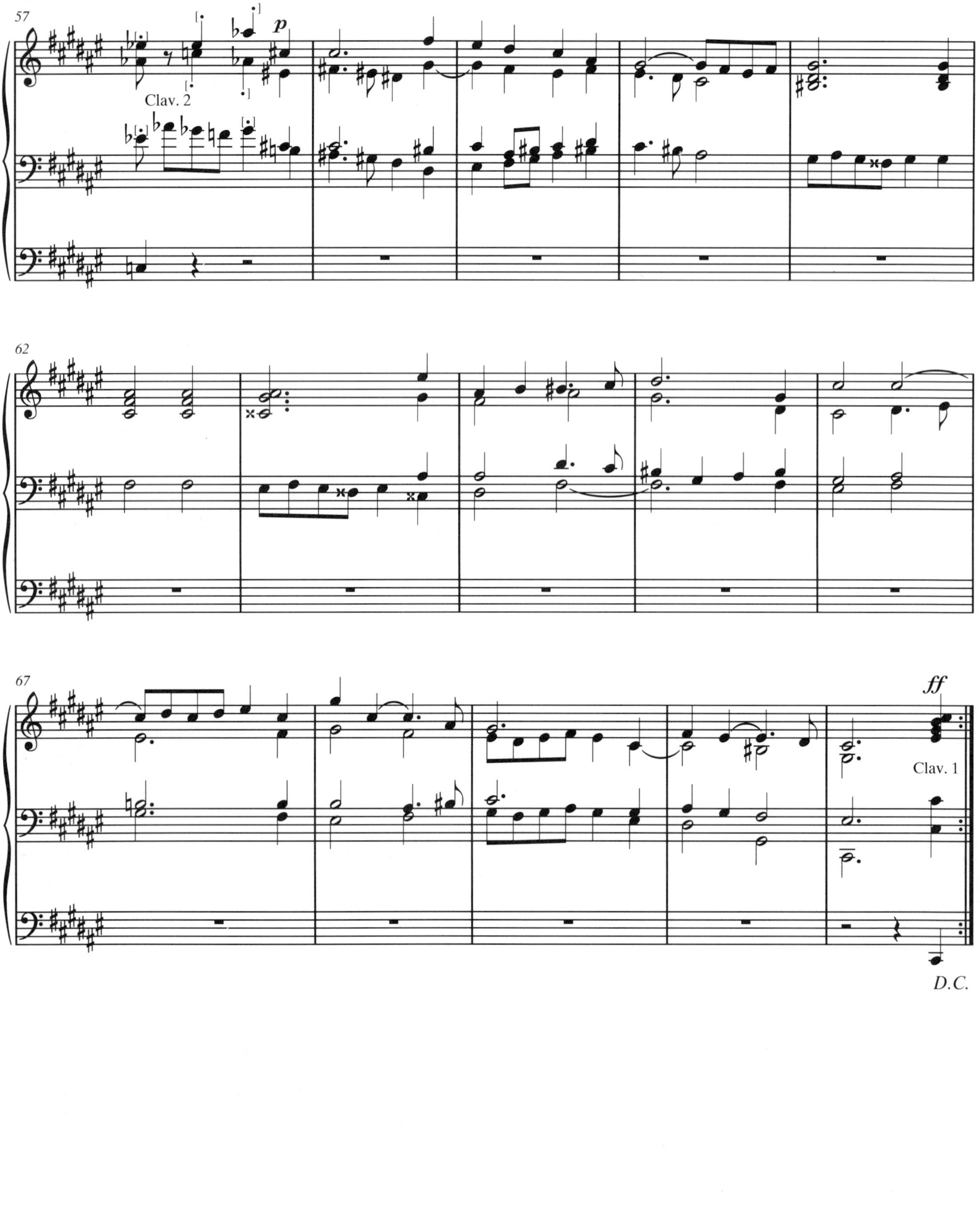
57
Clav. 2
p
62
67
ff
Clav. 1
D.C.

# Appendix 2
## III. Marcia

Version *B/B′*, Mm. 45–114, 139–43

*Version *B/B′*, m. 45 = version *D/E*, m. 45; version *B/B′*, m. 114 = version *D/E*, m. 134.

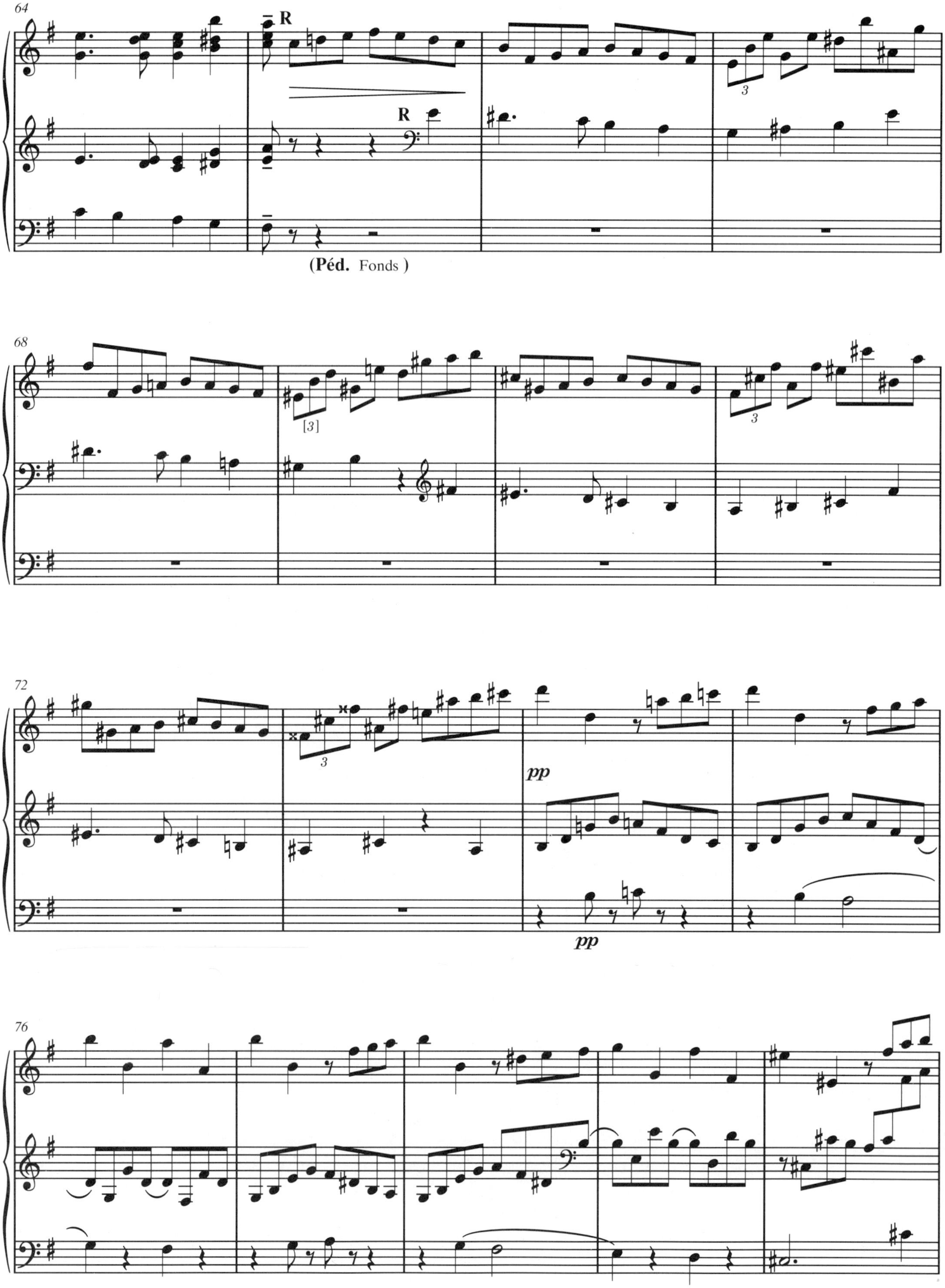
64
R
R
(Péd. Fonds )
68
[3]
72
pp
pp
76

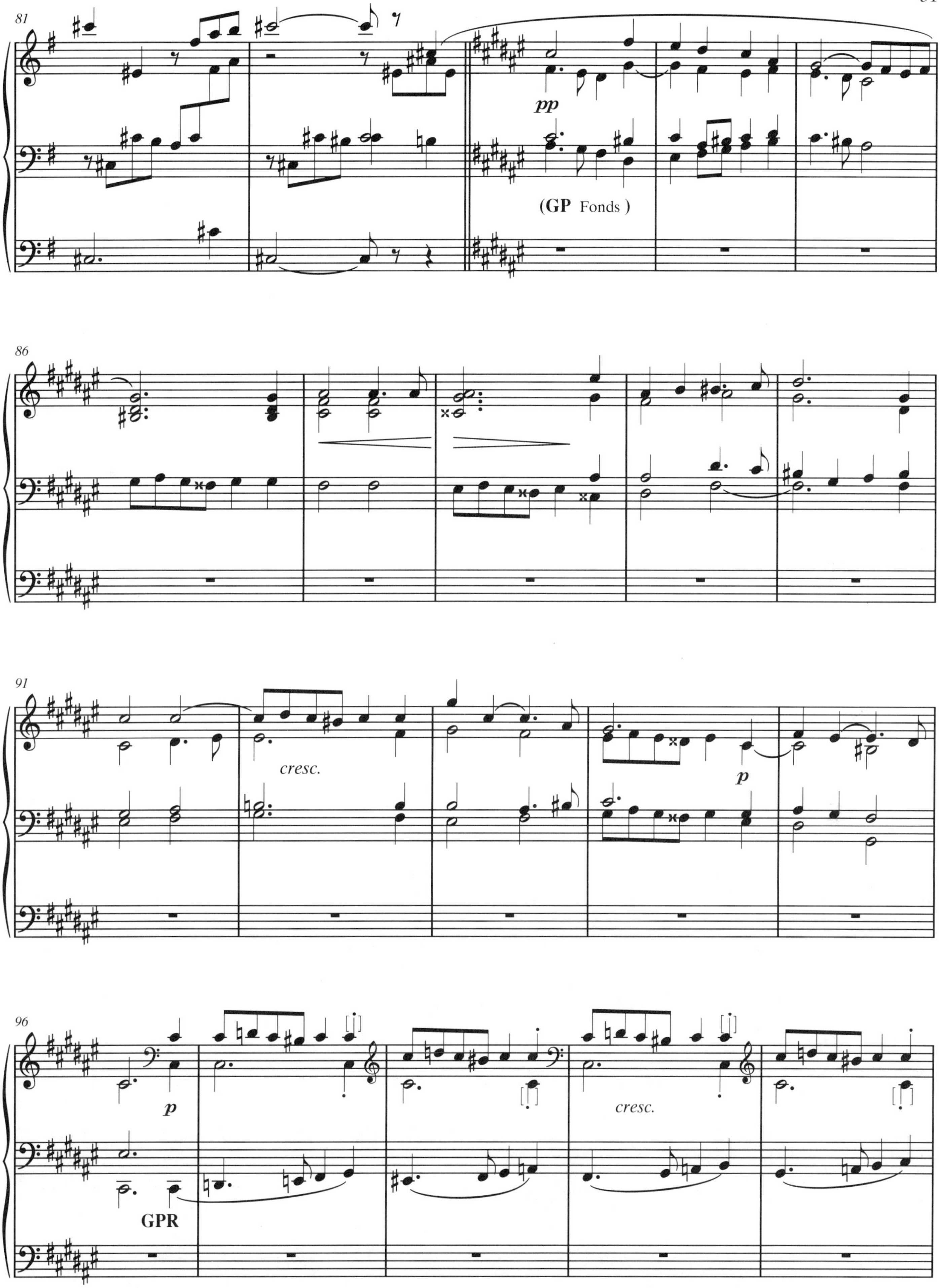
81
pp
(GP Fonds )
86
91
cresc.
p
96
p
cresc.
GPR

*Version B/B', m. 139 = version D/E, m. 159.

# Appendix 3
# III. Marcia

Editions *C* and *C'*, Mm. 75–96*

*Editions *C* and *C'*, m. 75 = version *D/E*, m. 75; editions *C* and *C'*, m. 96 = version *D/E*, m. 96.

54

Edition C':

C':

Appendix 4

# V. Fugue

Version *B/B′*

Grand orgue:  
Positif: } Fonds 8'  
Récit:  
Pédale: Fonds 16', 8'

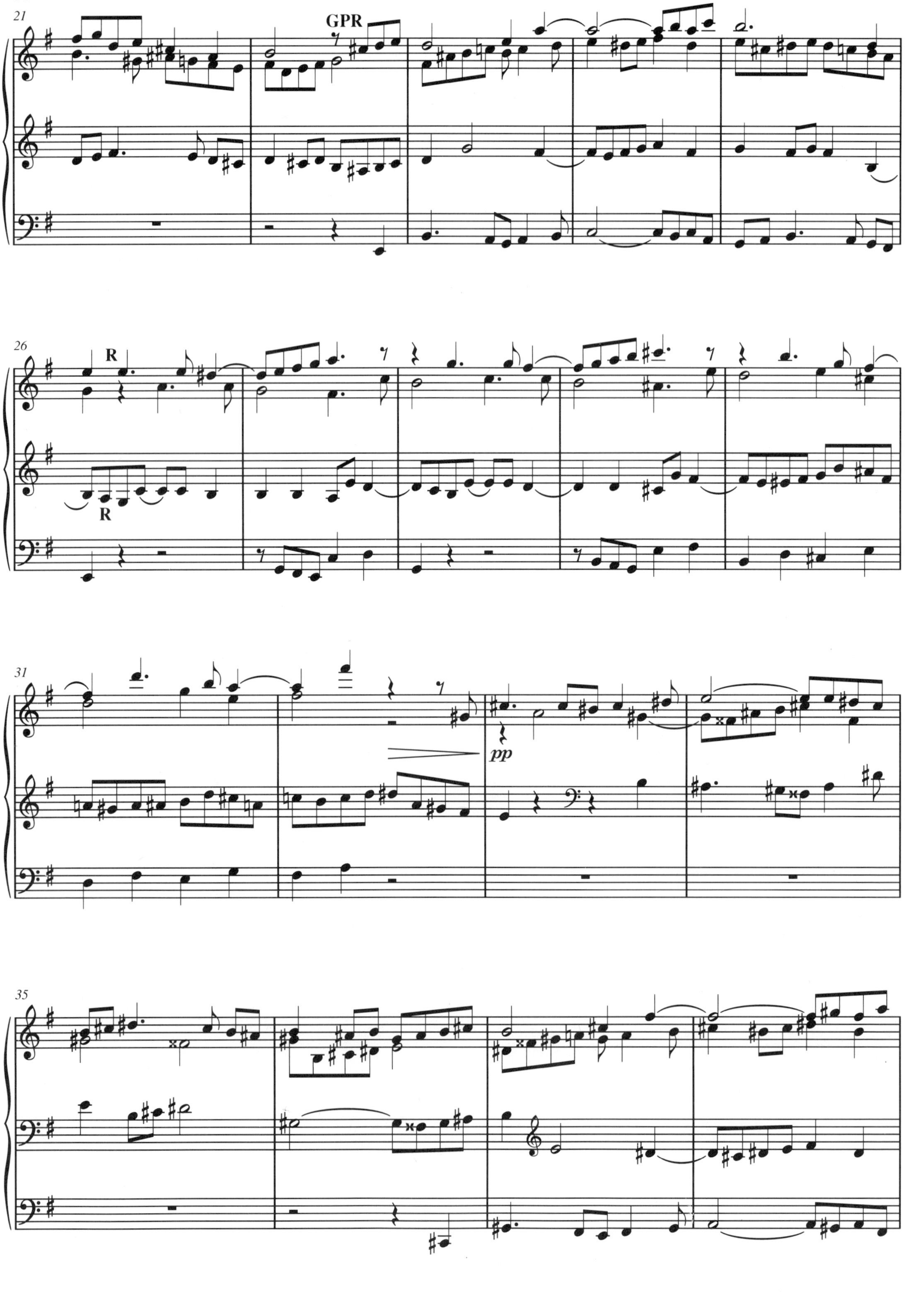
21
GPR
26
R
R
31
pp
35

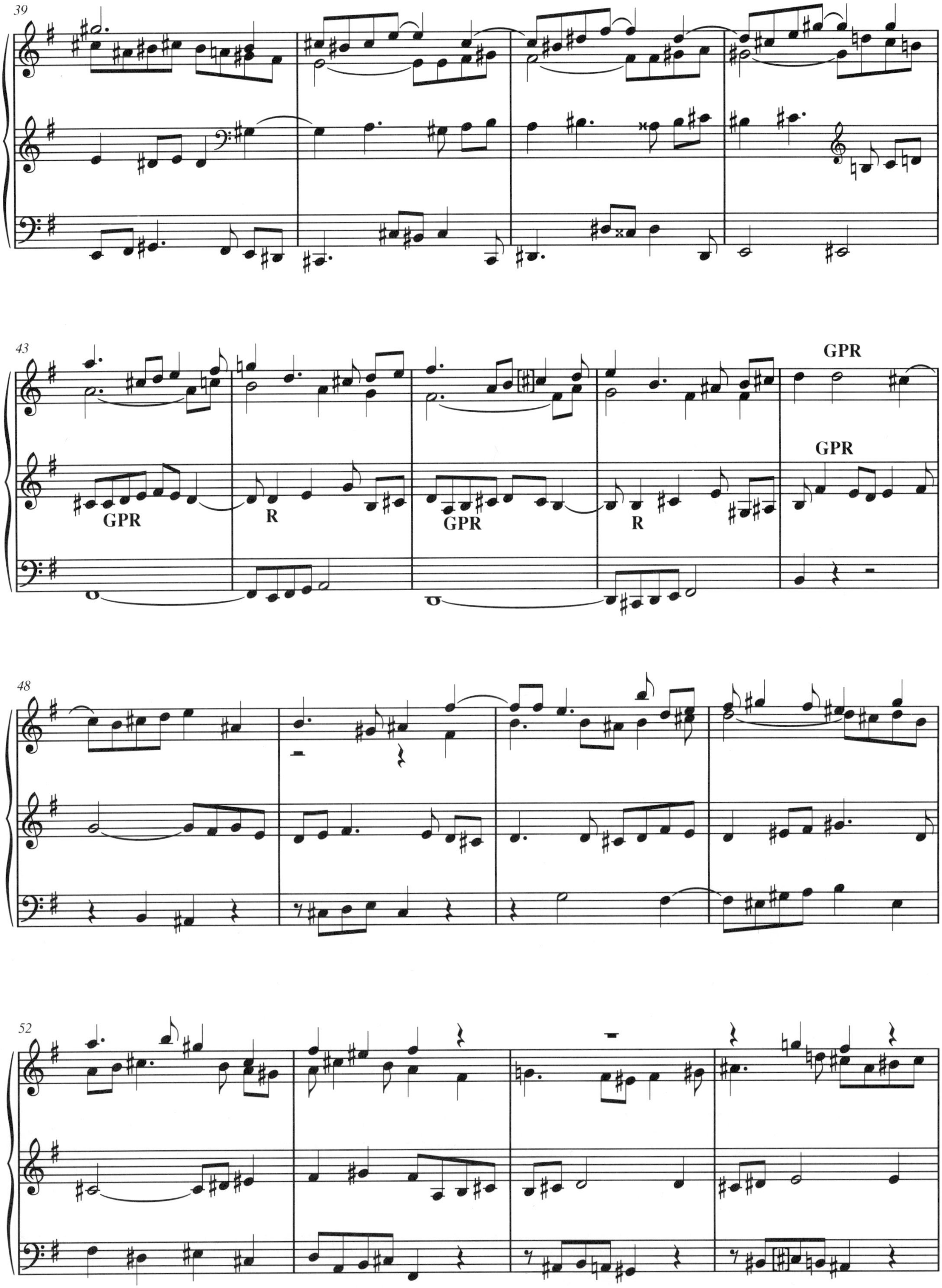
39
43
GPR
R
GPR
R
GPR
GPR
48
52

58

59

# VI. Finale

Appendix 5

Version *B/B'*

Grand orgue: Fonds 16', 8', 4'
Positif: Fonds 8'
Récit: Fonds et Anches 16', 8', 4'
Pédale: Basses 16', 8', 4'

**Allegro molto quasi presto** ($\textit{d}$ = 96)

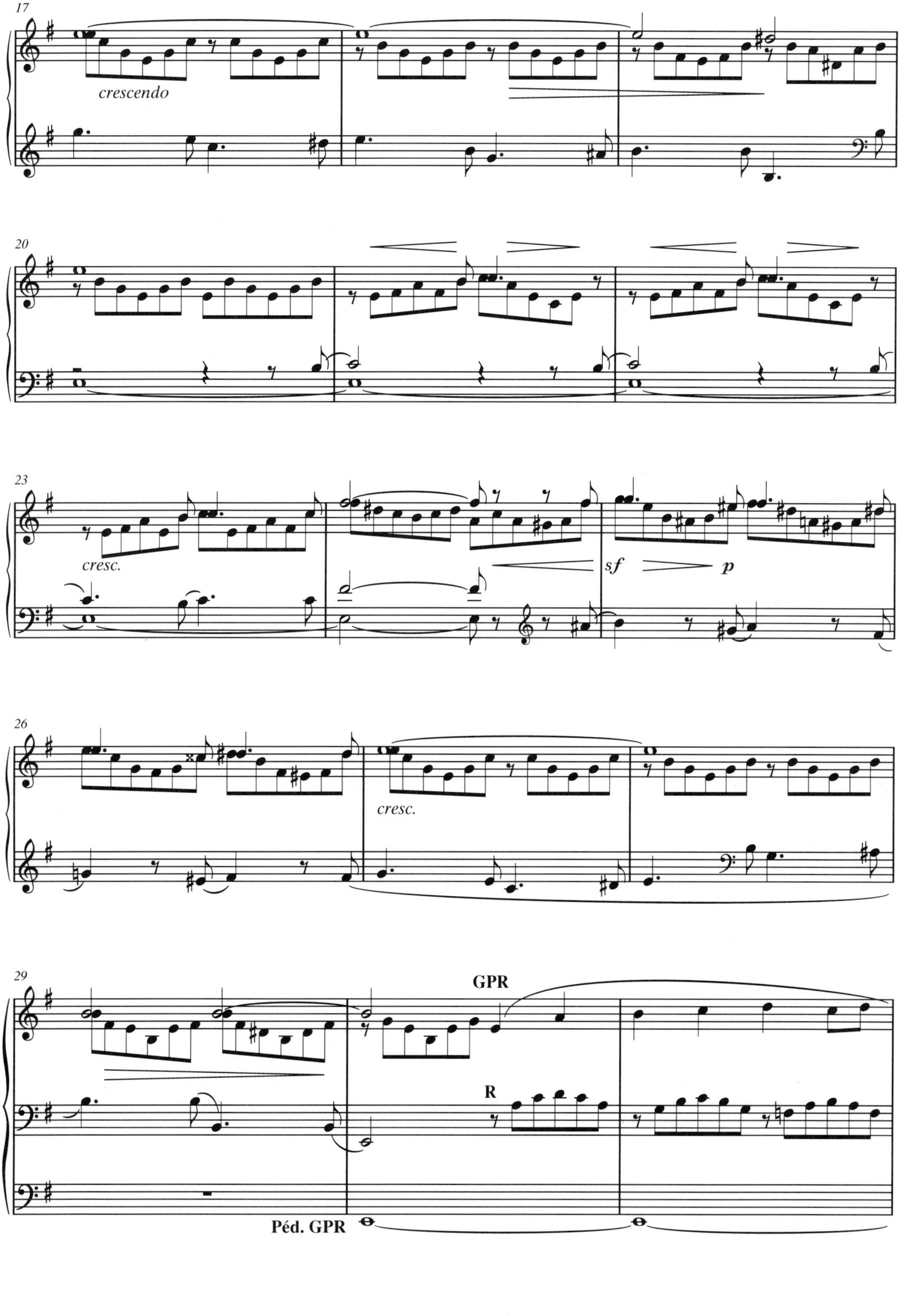
17
crescendo
20
23
cresc.
sf
p
26
cresc.
29
GPR
R
Péd. GPR

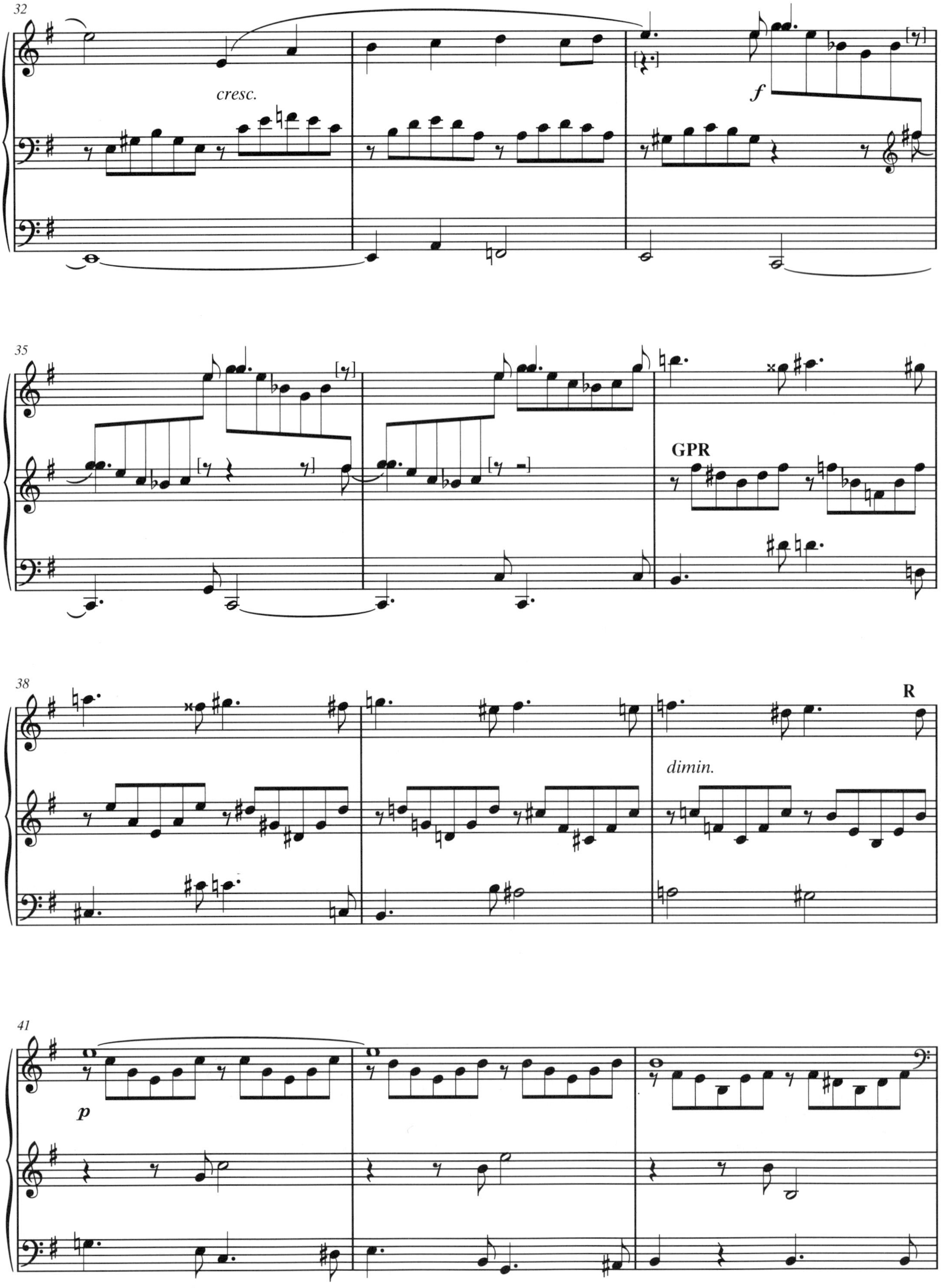
32
cresc.
f
35
GPR
38
R
dimin.
41
p

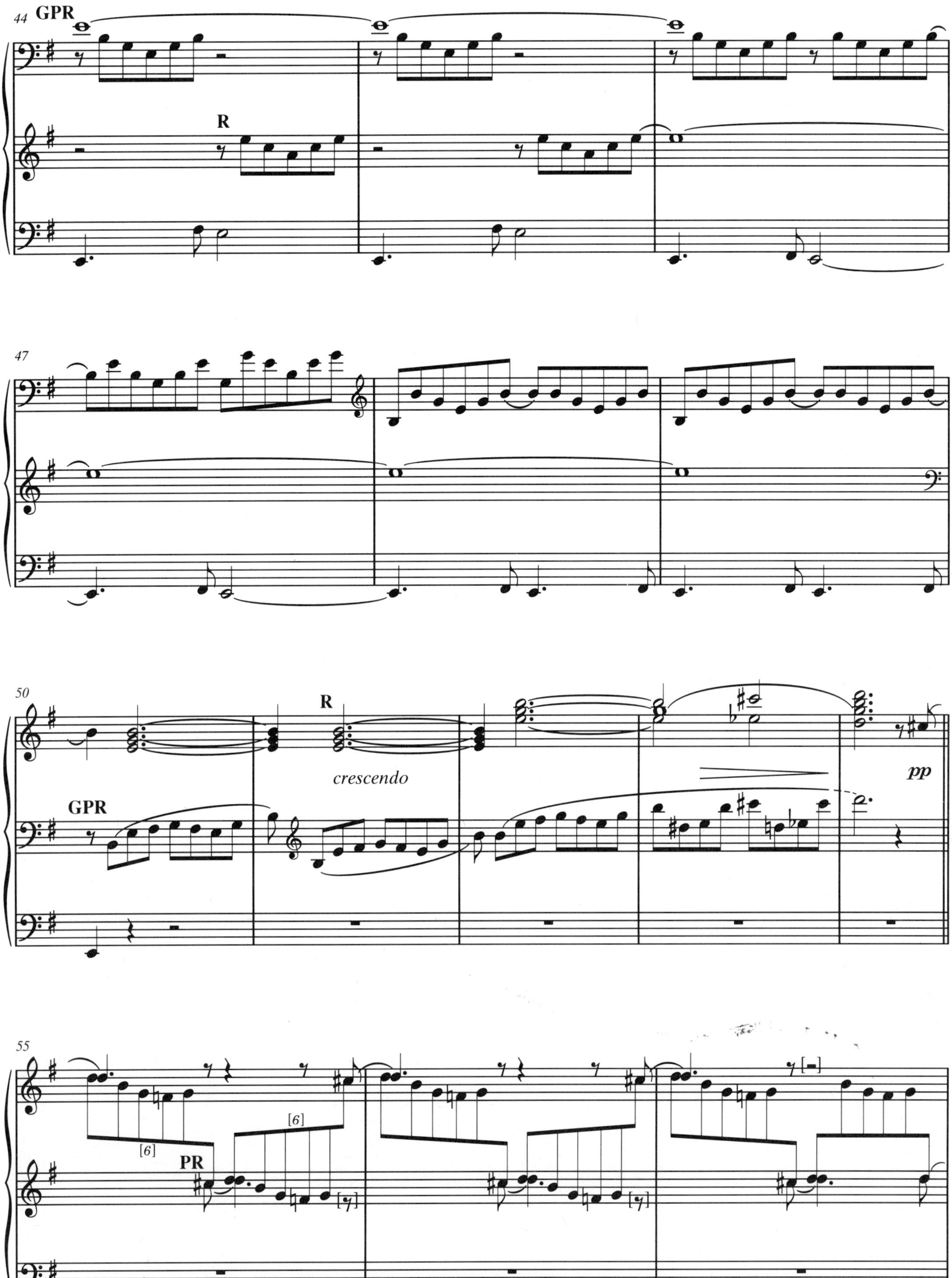
44
GPR
R
47
50
R
crescendo
GPR
pp
55
[6]
PR
[6]

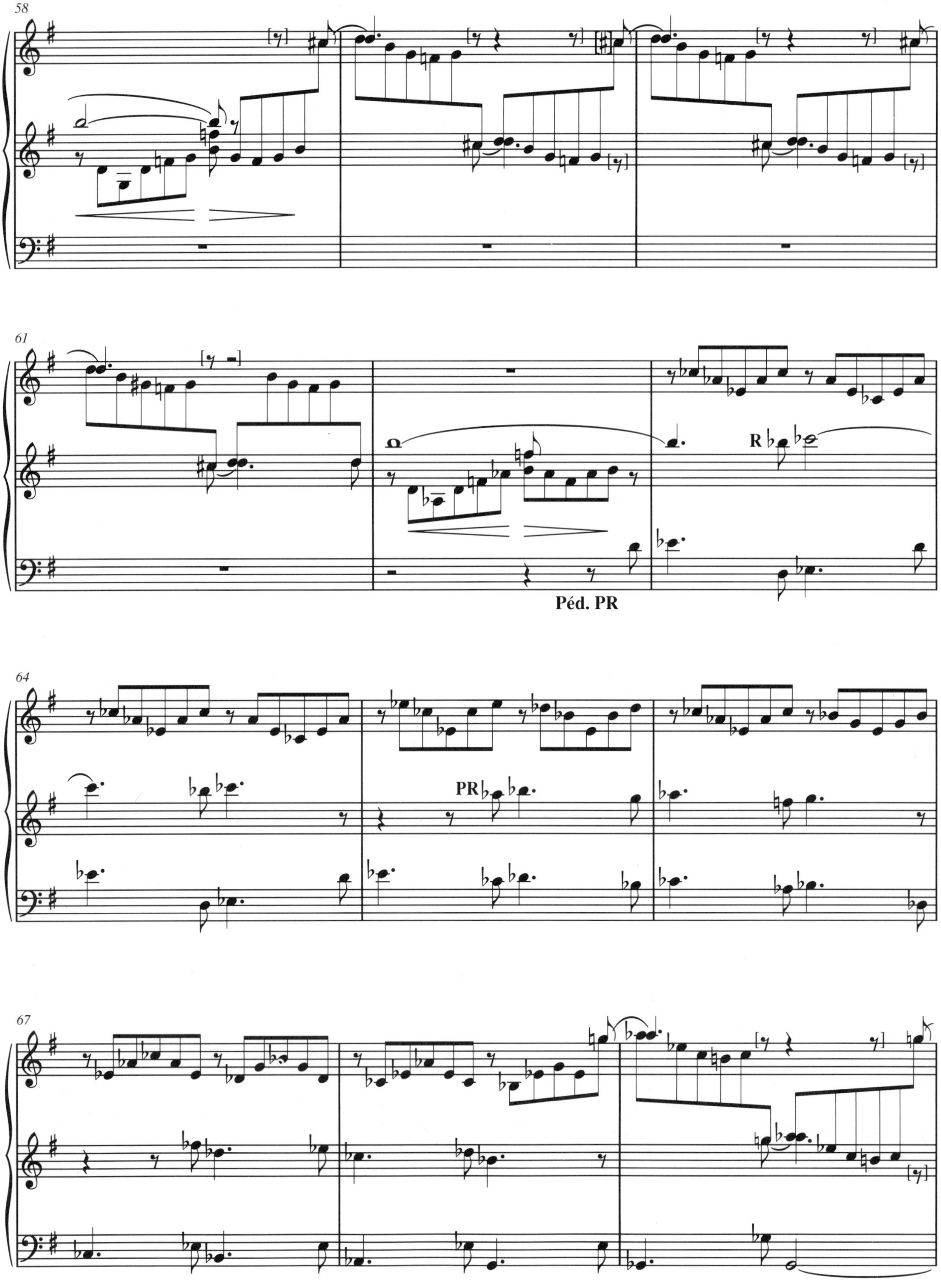
58
61
R
Péd. PR
64
PR
67

65

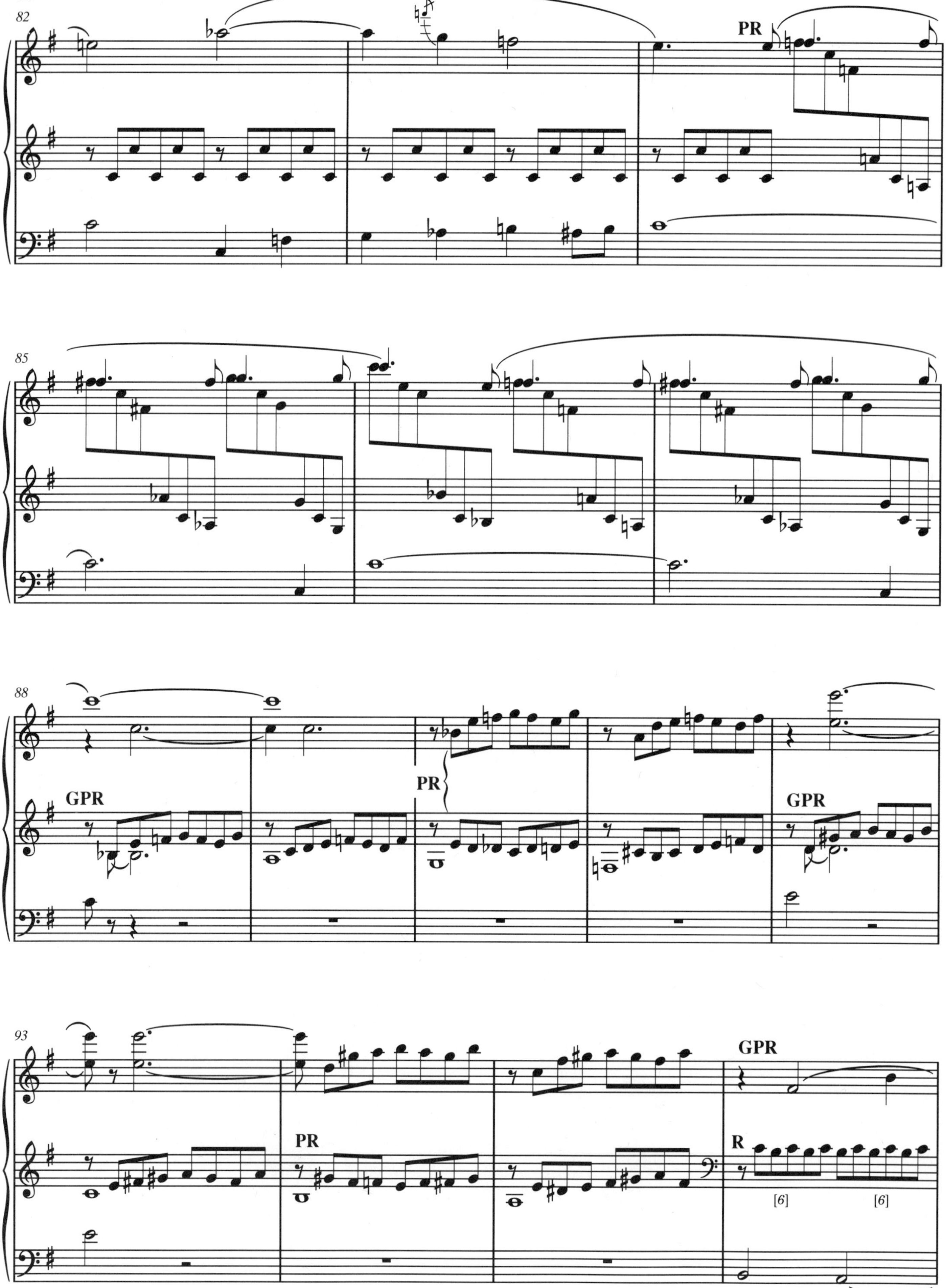
82
PR
85
88
GPR
PR
GPR
93
PR
GPR
R
[6]
[6]

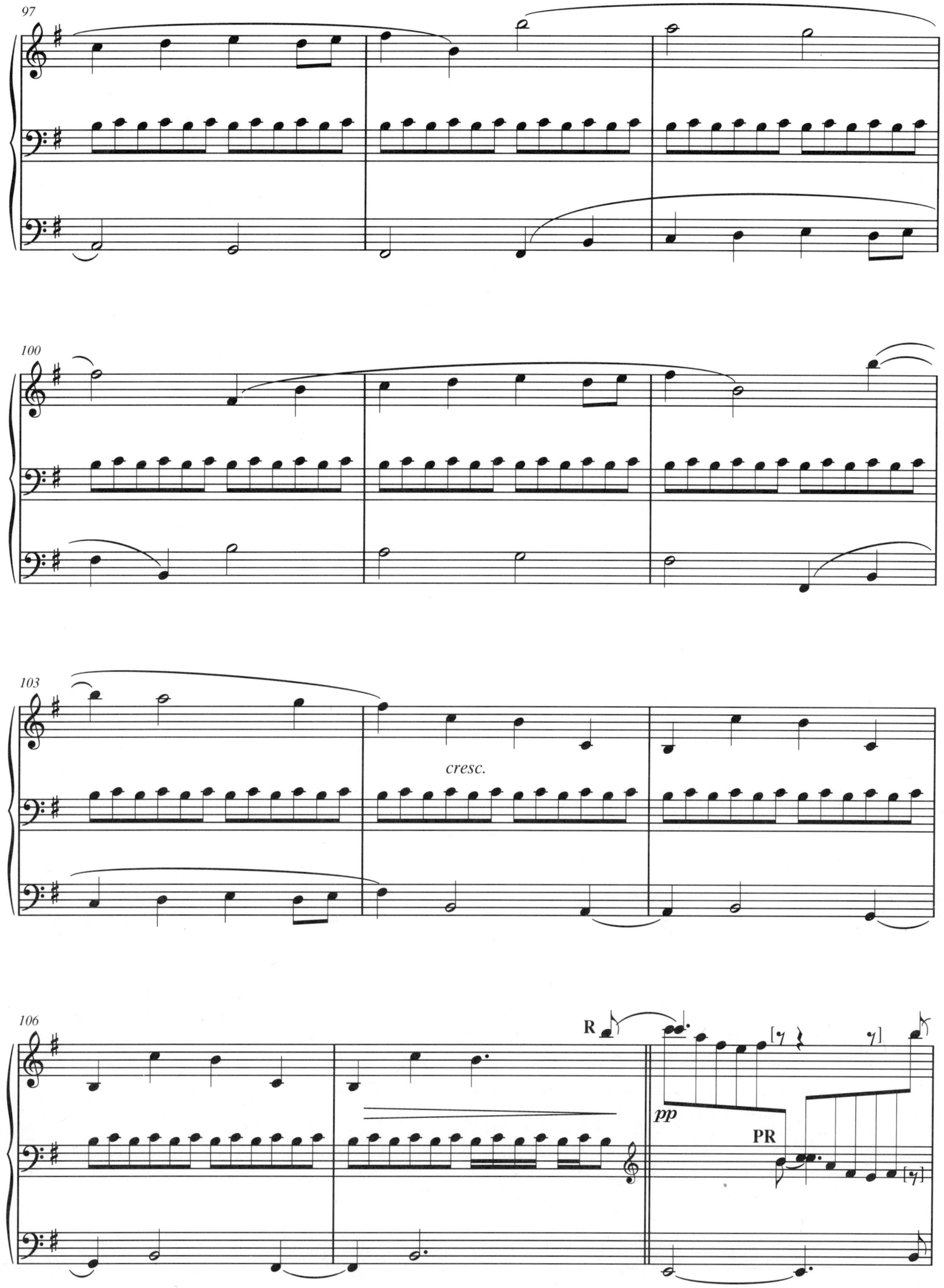
97
100
103
cresc.
106
R
pp
PR

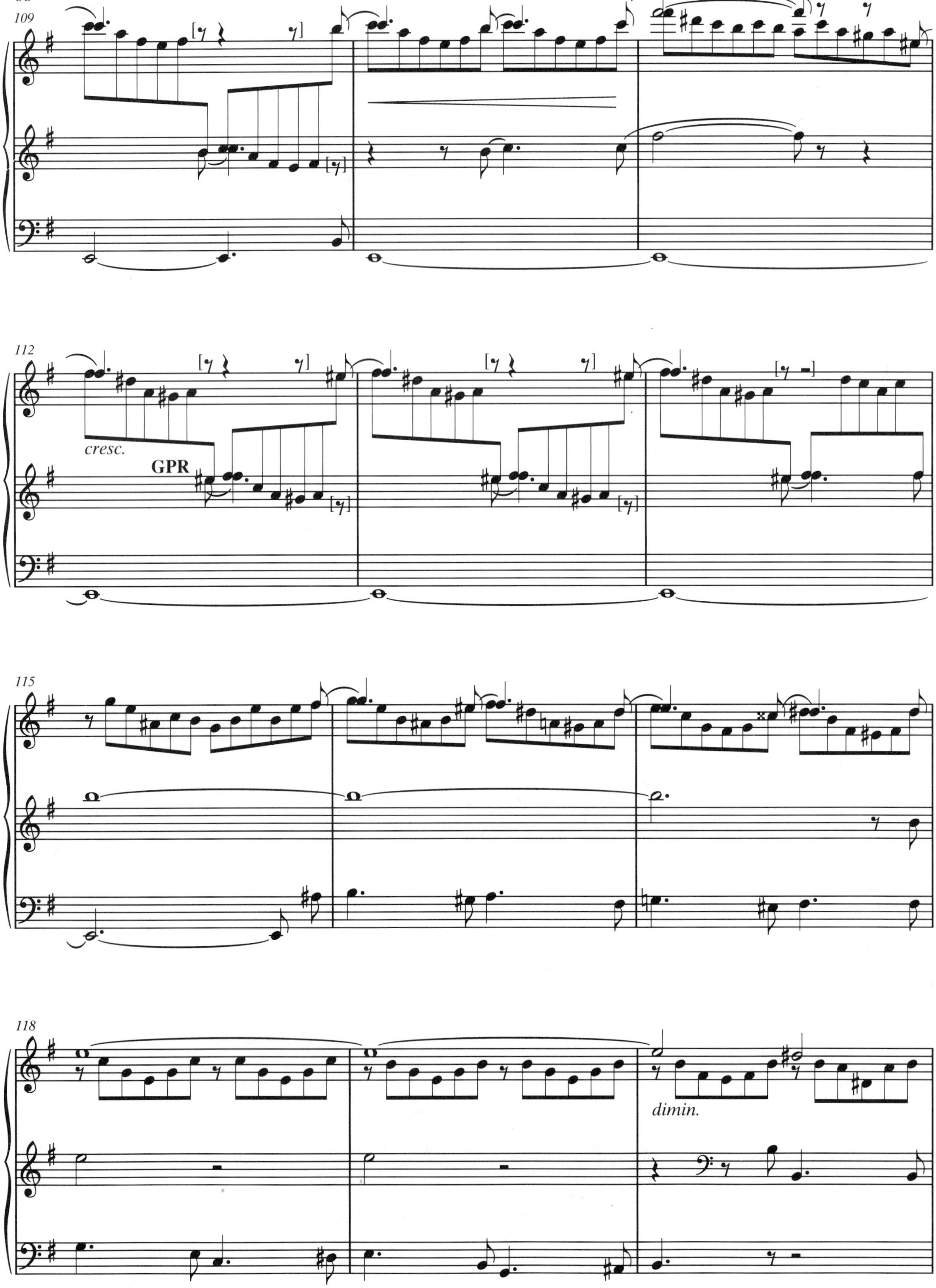
109
112
cresc.
GPR
115
118
dimin.

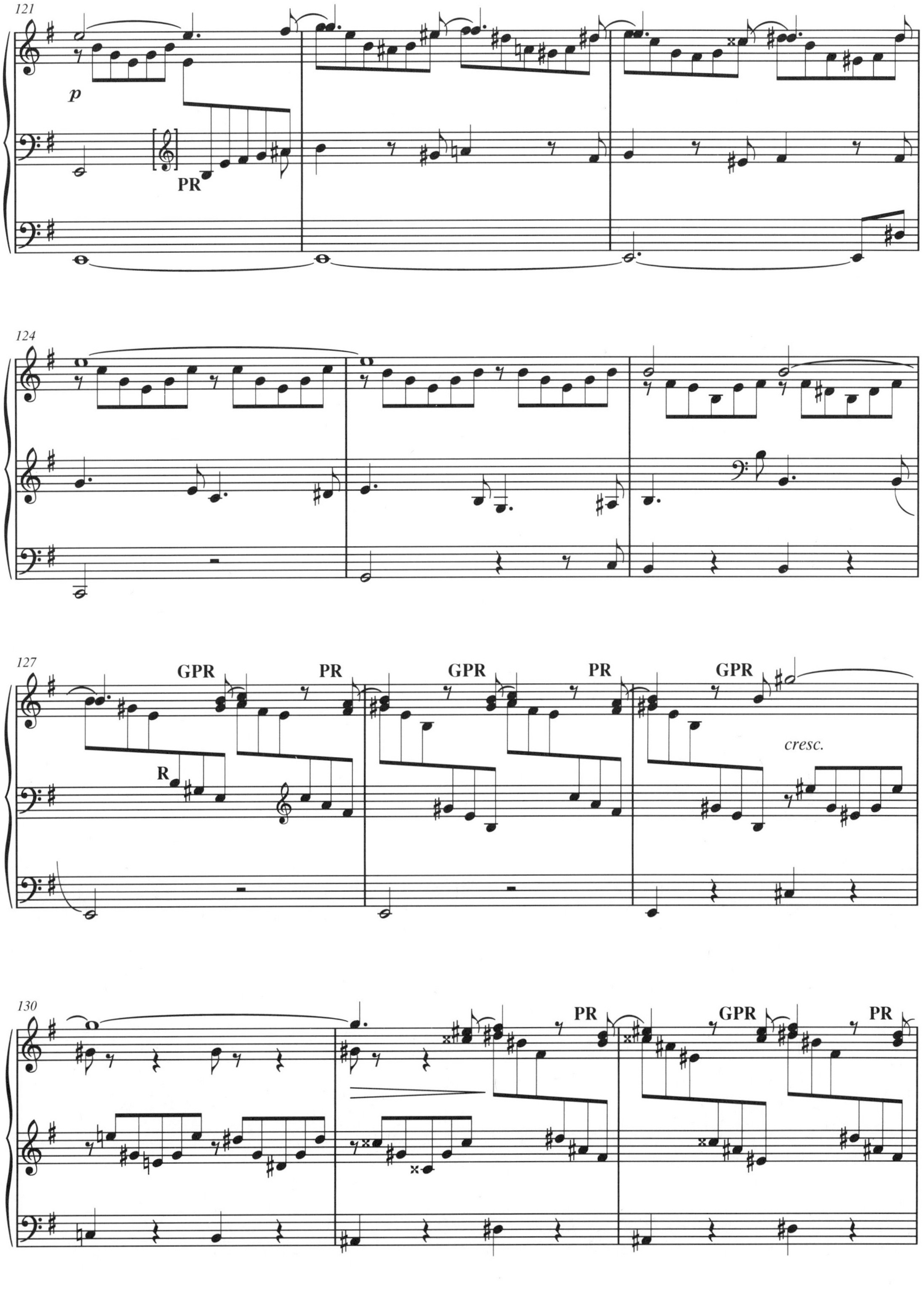
121
p
PR
124
127
GPR
PR
R
GPR
PR
GPR
cresc.
130
PR
GPR
PR

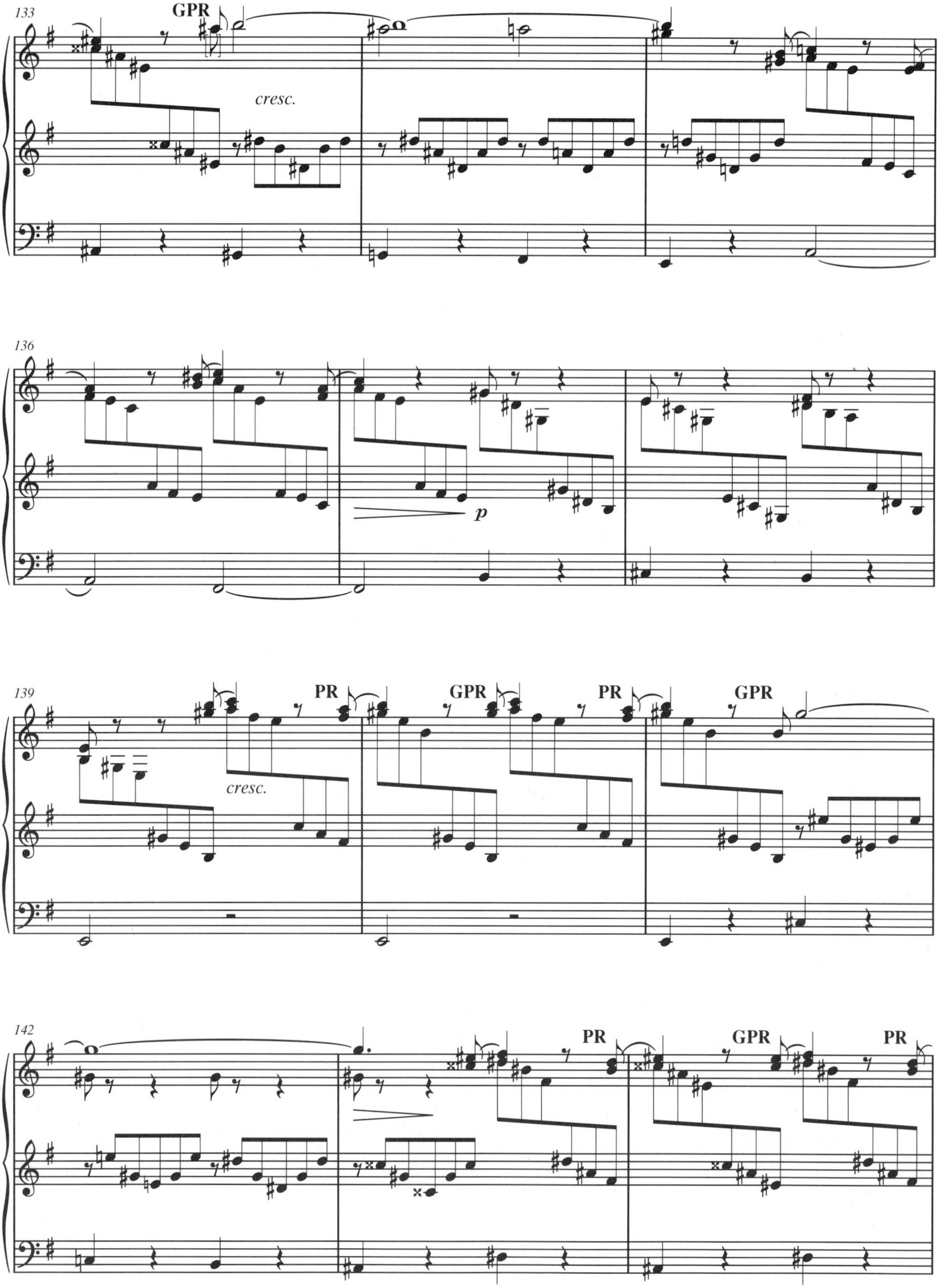
133
GPR
cresc.
136
p
139
PR
GPR
PR
GPR
cresc.
142
PR
GPR
PR

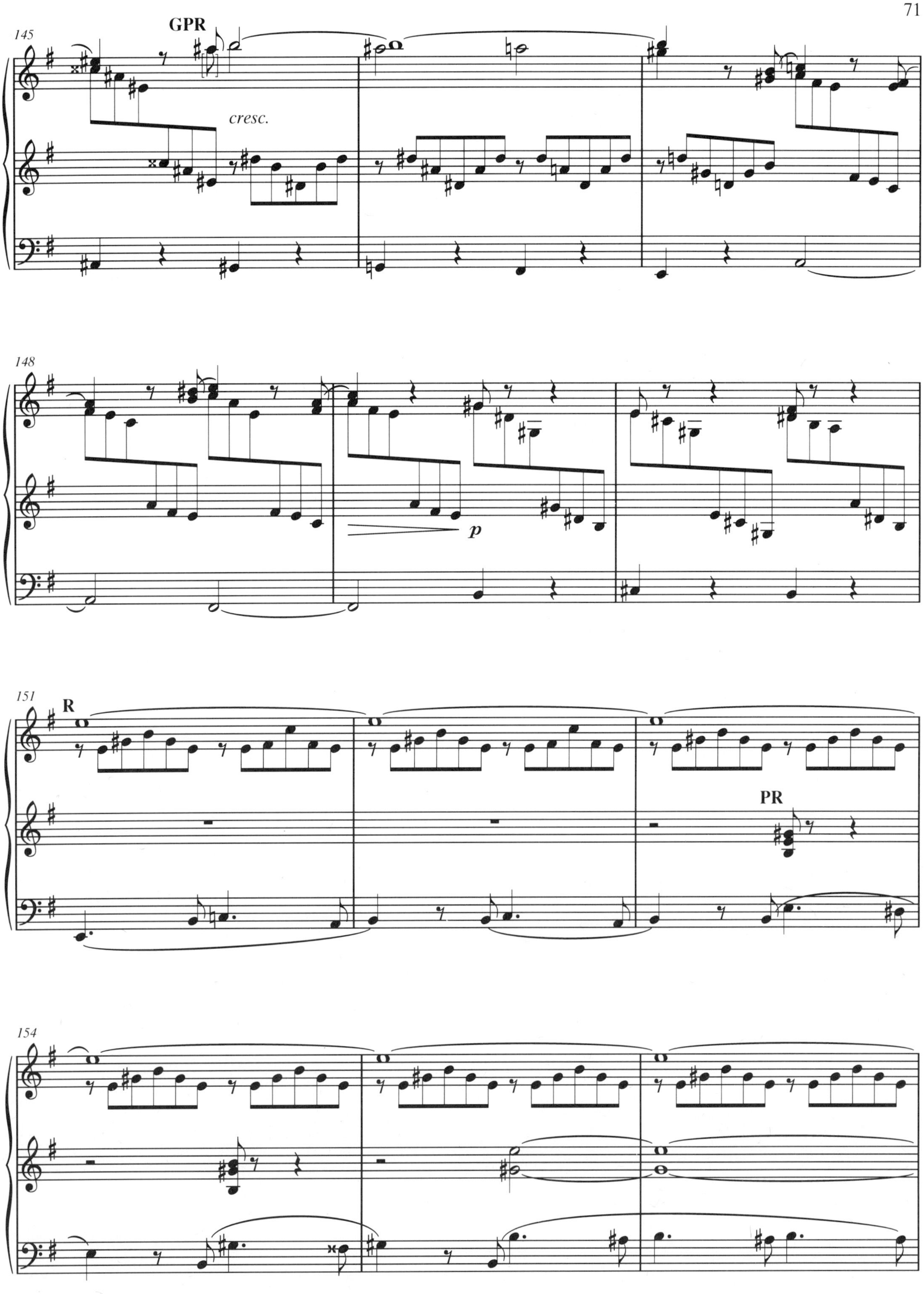
145
GPR
cresc.
148
p
151
R
PR
154

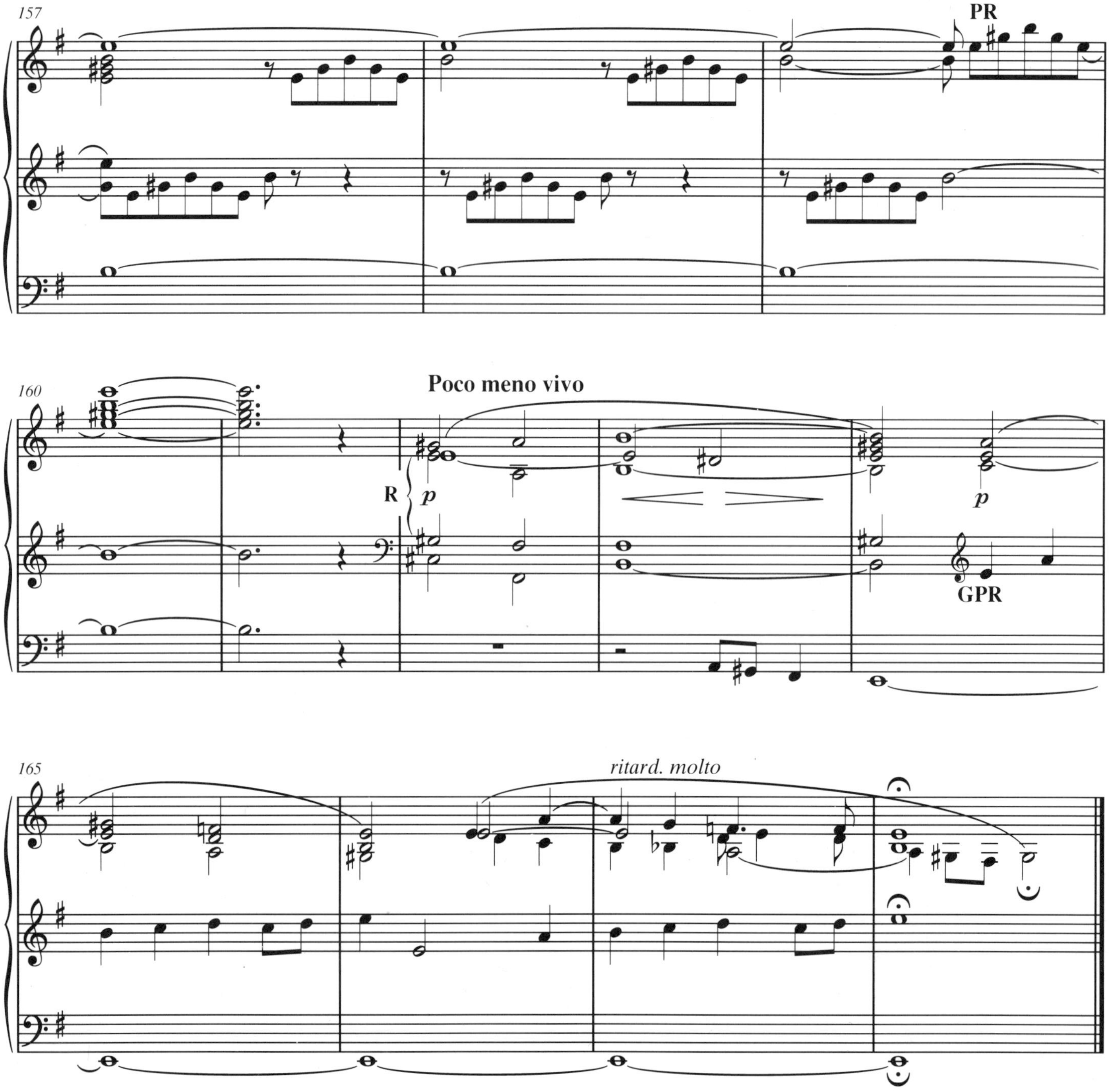
157
PR
160
Poco meno vivo
R
p
p
GPR
165
ritard. molto

# Appendix 6
# V. Final

Edition *C'*, Mm. 181–96*

*Edition *C'*, m. 181 = edition *E*, m. 181.

# Appendix 7
# V. Final

Edition D, Mm. 181–95*

*Edition D, m. 181 = edition E, m. 181.

DATE DUE

Demco, Inc. 38-293